HYPNOSIS

HYPNOSIS

by

L. CHERTOK, M.D.

Consultant Psychiatrist at the
Cochin Hospital, Paris

*Translated from an expanded version of the third
French edition in collaboration with the author
by*

D. GRAHAM

Senior Lecturer in Psychology,
University of Durham

PERGAMON PRESS

OXFORD · LONDON · EDINBURGH · NEW YORK
TORONTO · PARIS · FRANKFURT

Pergamon Press Ltd., Headington Hill Hall, Oxford
4 & 5 Fitzroy Square, London W.1

Pergamon Press (Scotland) Ltd., 2 & 3 Teviot Place, Edinburgh 1

Pergamon Press Inc., 44–01 21st Street, Long Island City, New York 11101

Pergamon of Canada Ltd., 6 Adelaide Street East, Toronto, Ontario

Pergamon Press S.A.R.L., 24 rue des Ecoles, Paris 5[e]

Pergamon Press GmbH, Kaiserstrasse 75, Frankfurt-am-Main

First edition 1966

Library of Congress Catalog Card No. 64-66210

Filmset by Graphic Film Limited Dublin Ireland
Printed and bound in Great Britain by
Thomas Nelson (Printers) Ltd.,
London and Edinburgh.
2401/66

Contents

FOREWORD TO THE ENGLISH EDITION   vii
FOREWORD   ix
INTRODUCTION   xiii
PART ONE: THEORETICAL AND PRACTICAL PROBLEMS
  HISTORICAL SURVEY   3
  THEORIES OF HYPNOSIS   12
  PAVLOVIAN THEORY   16
  THEORIES INSPIRED BY EXPERIMENTAL PSYCHOLOGY   19
  PSYCHOANALYTIC THEORIES   29
  HYPNOSIS AND SLEEP   40
  ANIMAL HYPNOSIS   42
  HYPNOTIZABILITY   48
  APPLICATIONS   54
  HYPNOSIS AND PSYCHOANALYSIS   64
  INSTRUCTION IN HYPNOSIS   69
  INDICATIONS   72
PART TWO: TECHNIQUES OF HYPNOSIS
  INTRODUCTION   95
  THE PREPARATORY TALK   97
  TESTS OF SUGGESTIBILITY   99
  INDUCTION   101
  DEEPENING THE TRANCE   111
  AWAKENING THE PATIENT   119
  THE SUBJECT'S EXPERIENCE OF THE TRANCE   120
  HYPNOSIS WITH DRUGS   122
  SPECIALIZED TECHNIQUES   124
  AUTOHYPNOSIS   128
  GROUP HYPNOSIS   132
  HYPNODRAMA   134
PART THREE: TECHNIQUES DERIVED FROM HYPNOSIS   139
CONCLUSION   153
BIBLIOGRAPHY   157
NAME INDEX   169
SUBJECT INDEX   172

Foreword to the English edition

INTEREST in hypnosis seems to be a cyclic phenomenon. Following the Second World War, in part because of the use of hypnosis in the treatment of psychiatric combat casualties, American psychiatry began to occupy itself in this area from a somewhat different perspective. The Council on Mental Health of the American Medical Association through its Commission on Hypnosis served as a stimulus to this fresh look. Books and articles are being published. Several National Societies were organized in this special field in the United States. In France, the country of Liébeault, Bernheim, Charcot, curiously enough, hypnosis has been completely discarded. Dr. Leon Chertok, author of this volume, interested in utilization of hypnosis within a psychoanalytic frame of reference tried to renew interest in his country and to show that it is not an anachronism and still a worthwhile field of research. It is with this in mind that the author wrote this book, the first on this subject in French after more than half a century.

This book, translated from the French, should prove a welcome addition to the current literature on the subject. It is to be commended for its historical perspective and elegant simplicity, and for providing a concise, compact yet comprehensive view of hypnosis in its various aspects.

M. RALPH KAUFMAN, M.D.

Director, Department of Psychiatry
Institute of Psychiatry
The Mount Sinai Hospital
New York, New York

Clinical Professor of Psychiatry
College of Physicians and Surgeons
Columbia University
New York, New York

Professor of Psychiatry
The Mount Sinai Medical School
New York, New York

Foreword

To HYPNOTIZE someone is to exert some kind of power or influence over him which renders him amenable to suggestion. But the power of the hypnotist requires the weakness or unconscious co-operation of the hypnotized subject. This means that the "trance", the state of "induced somnambulism", the "hypnotic sleep", may be obtained by techniques which seek to increase either the force of the suggestion or the degree of suggestibility.

The conditions for the suggestion-value of the therapeutic act clearly depend upon the personality of the hypnotist, not so much as he is, but as he appears to be; that is, we have here a psychotherapeutic relationship. The transference here is intense and "wild", rather like a "fluid", the effect of which is inescapable if not overwhelming (through Charcot and Braid we reach Mesmer and Puységur). It is not surprising that the development of this immediate transference into a controlled process extending over time, and the use of language for communication between therapist and patient, led Freud to his discovery.

The conditions of suggestibility naturally depend upon the neurosis itself and especially upon hysterical elements involved in it. Not every subject is easily hypnotized, and this fact gives rise to the practical value of techniques for the attainment of a state favourable to hypnosis. A sort of "trick" is introduced into the practice of hypnosis, which depends upon "mental power". This is the use, no longer of the *placebo* of imagination, but of psychopharmacological agents which have the effect of reducing vigilance (barbiturates, scopochloralose, pentothal and so on). These narcotherapeutic methods give the experience of hypnosis its full significance in the neuroses. To the negative condition of the patient, they add what the neurosis itself cannot provide. This involves an "experience" and a "technique" in which mental and physical factors are both involved and which are relevant to essentially psychosomatic states. It was for this reason that Dr. Chertok, a specialist in this field, became particularly interested in this problem.

I should like to say just o.ie further word to the reader before he embarks upon the study of this strange and still rather mysterious psychosomatic process. From the point of view of deontology and morality, it has been asked whether this "violation of the personality", this "assault", this subjection of the patient to the hypnotist, is permissible. If it were true that only the hypnotist counted and the subject was of no importance, if it were a case of being "swallowed whole", like a frog hypnotized by a snake, then such complete absorption would be nothing short of monstrous. But it is not like this at all, for the hypnotist has no power beyond that which is unconsciously conferred upon him by the subject. It follows that the problem is really this. Is one entitled to use a man's unconscious in order to relieve him of his unconscious burden? It seems to me that to ask the question in this way is virtually to answer it in the affirmative, for it is surely permissible (and indeed it would be absurd if it were not) for a doctor with the end of curing his patient in view, to use the available means (in this case, hypnosis) to attain it. This argument in fact holds for all procedures or techniques which involve *operating upon* the patient, even in spite of himself, to cure his illness (biological and psychosurgical treatments, narco-analysis, use of hypnotic drugs or psychoanalytic treatment).

I do not know whether the revival of hypnosis will mean the revival of these controversial issues, but this book is certain to arouse a great deal of interest.

HENRI EY

Principal Psychiatrist,
Hôpital psychiatrique Bonneral

Secretary-general,
World Psychiatric Association

"Falling as it does between the normal functioning of the organism and the disorders which are the natural consequence of illness, hypnotism provides a convenient approach for research. The hypnotic state is nothing but an artificial or experimentally induced nervous state ... the many manifestations of which appear or disappear at the will of the experimenter, according to the demands of his research ... Viewed in this way, hypnotism represents an extremely promising field for research for physiologists and psychologists as well as for medical practitioners."

CHARCOT-RICHER (*Arch. Neur.,* 1881, 2, p. 33)

"Hypnosis is the crossroads for all levels of physiological and psychological organization, and ... the phenomenon which we call hypnotism when more fully understood will be one of our most important tools for the study of normal sleep, of normal alertness, and of the continuous interplay among normal, neurotic, and psychotic processes."

L. KUBIE (*Arch. gen. Psychiat.,* 1961, 4, p. 53)

Introduction

THE passages which we have quoted on the previous page promise hypnosis a brilliant future. As the progenitor of most modern psychotherapies, hypnosis has already demonstrated its fruitfulness. It is now called upon to play a major role in experimental psychopathology and psychotherapy. Eighty years have passed since Charcot made his predictions, and we still do not know the precise nature of hypnosis. None of the theories which have so far been advanced provide more than a partial explanation. We do not even have objective criteria of whether a subject is hypnotized or not. Hypnosis is a fluid, fleeting and elusive phenomenon and yet a phenomenon of undeniable reality. All these features emphasize the fascination of the subject. And yet, after a period of glory in France at the end of the last century, hypnosis was completely forgotten there. Elsewhere, however, and especially in the United States and the Soviet Union, hypnosis and its applications have been the subject of an ever-increasing attention.

The golden age of hypnosis (1880–90) is also the period when French medicine was at its most flourishing. During this period, hypnosis in France benefited by being officially recognized by the medical schools. Many great doctors of the period were interested in and studied hypnosis. The first International Congress of Experimental and Therapeutic Hypnotism was held at the Hôtel-Dieu hospital in Paris, from 8th to 12th August 1889, with Charcot, Brown-Séquart, Brouardel, Charles Richet, Azam, Lombroso and Mesnet as honorary presidents. Among the participants, in addition to Liébeault and Bernheim, were Déjerine, Janet, Babinski, Forel, Magnan, Freud, Schrenck-Notzing, William James and Bechterev. The effective president of the Congress was Dumontpallier, head of department at the Hôtel-Dieu hospital and secretary-general of the Société de Biologie.

The period of decline began with the death of Charcot (1893).

As evidence of this decline, it may be noted that the *Revue de l'Hypnotisme expérimental et thérapeutique,* which appeared under this name from 1886 to 1889, in 1890 assumed the name of *Revue de l'Hypnotisme et de la Psychologie physiologique,* became in 1909 the *Revue de la Psychothérapie et de Psychologie appliquée* and as such appeared until 1914, and finally reappeared from 1922 until 1934 under the name of the *Revue de Psychologie appliquée.*

The eclipse was complete; the very existence of hypnotic phenomena almost came to be denied. Babinski (7) could thus declare that hypnosis, like hysteria, was a kind of simulation. These views, indeed, still receive strong support among some medical men. And it is significant that our friend Koupernik some years ago in a report in a weekly paper on the visit of a stage hypnotist,* considered it necessary to assert vigorously the very existence of hypnotic phenomena.

Janet, in 1923, believed that the decline of hypnosis was only a "transient eclipse" (105, p. 204), "a passing accident . . . in the history of psychotherapy" (104, p. 30). Again, he maintained that "when there will have been a new turn of fashion's wheel . . . it will bring back treatment by hypnotic suggestion just as it will bring back our grandmothers' hats" (105, p. 151). Janet was the only one to maintain some interest in hypnosis. We should not, however, forget to mention another writer, Parcheminey (166), who in 1932 embarked upon the study of hypnosis from the point of view of psychoanalysis. Although in other countries there has been a renewal of interest in hypnosis, in France the number of publications on the subject during the past half-century has been exceedingly small. The problem of hypnosis seems to have been shelved in France.

In the first part of the book, we shall give a brief historical survey, outline the theoretical problems, study the relationship between hypnosis and sleep, give a chapter on animal hypnosis and consider the question of hypnotizability, and then discuss some therapeutic applications and indications and the question

---

*It should be remembered that it was after attending public demonstrations of hypnosis that certain well-known doctors became interested in hypnotic phenomena. Thus Braid started his work after having witnessed the demonstrations given at Manchester by the celebrated magnetizer of the age, Lafontaine. Freud declared that he had become convinced of the reality of hypnotic phenomena after having seen Hansen at work; while Charcot, similarly, was influenced by the demonstrations of Donato.

of teaching. The second part will give a compact account of hypnotic techniques (nothing has been published in France describing techniques since the classic work of Bernheim and Liébeault). The third part is devoted to techniques derived from hypnosis.

L. C.

PART ONE

THEORETICAL AND PRACTICAL PROBLEMS

Historical Survey

THE entry of psychology into the field of medical science was very stormy. As is well known, it was marked at the end of the eighteenth century by violent arguments, echoes of which can still be heard today. This controversy may legitimately be held to have started with the discoveries of Mesmer, who began operating with "magnetic" metals, and thence gradually elaborated the theory of animal magnetism (151, 152, 153). According to him, a beneficial magnetic fluid could be transmitted from one subject to another. After the establishment of "rapport" between therapist and patient, and more or less prolonged manipulation of the latter by "passes", the operator effected a therapeutic "crisis" (a sort of convulsive seizure). Particular attention was paid to the setting of collective sessions (what we should today call group psychotherapy); the master wore lilac silk robes and music played an important part (Mesmer was the friend of Mozart and was responsible for the introduction into France of . . . the mouth-organ!).

Such a complex personality could not but be a controversial figure; Mesmer had both adherents and detractors, but however open to criticism he may have been, he must be allowed to have been the first to undertake an experimental study of the psychotherapeutic relationship, which until then had been obscured in magical practices. It must be remembered that in the eighteenth century, the century of the Encyclopaedists, superstition, witchcraft and many other esoteric practices still flourished. Witches were still being burned, the last one being put to death in 1782. Mesmer, who was a cultured man, put forward a theory which he believed to be physiological and rational, positing the existence of a fluid as real and as material as, for example, the action of a magnet.

Mesmer did not, however, identify the action of animal magnetism with that of the magnet, and protested against such interpretations made by critics who accused him of plagiarizing Paracelsus. He had abandoned the use of the magnet in 1776, and in 1779 he wrote that animal magnetism was "essentially distinct

3

from the magnet" (151, p. 35). Again, in the same work, in connexion with the interesting results obtained by the use of the magnet, he wrote, "Another principle was causing the magnet to act, the magnet itself being incapable of such action on the nerves and I saw that I only had a short way to go in order to arrive at the *imitative theory* which formed the subject of my search" (op. cit., pp. 34–35). According to Voutsinas (228), this "imitative theory" refers simply to suggestion, of which Mesmer had had some idea, but which he had not been able to formulate properly. A few years later, Mesmer expressed himself less clearly, saying that "man has properties analogous to those of a magnet" (153, p. 6), and that "the magnet provides a model of the working of the universe" (p. 28). Puységur, in 1813, took the following view. "The word 'magnet', like 'density', 'electricity', 'gravity', etc., is a conventional term adopted to facilitate mutual understanding, and does not indicate a substance" (178, p. 7)*.

In spite of the rationalist tendencies of Mesmer, the public was interested in his experiments for motives of a different kind. The end of the eighteenth century coincided in France with the appearance of romantic sensibility, in which the demands of feeling, long contained by the rationalist imperatives, sought proper satisfaction. Mesmer's experiments were conducted in a most favourable setting and his magnetic fluid at once acquired mystical significance.

Although "rapport" existed in Mesmer's procedures, the master did not bother much about it; he was interested only in physiology. When the Marquis de Puységur (177, 178) told Mesmer about his discovery of induced somnambulism and the possibility of entering into verbal communication with the subject, Mesmer minimized the importance of the phenomenon. He already knew of the existence of such a phenomenon but did not pay much attention to it. He wanted to remain in the field of physiology; and he may be regarded as the founder of the physiological trend in the explanation of hypnosis. Psychology was for Mesmer a product of the imagination and, as such, difficult to study.

In psychoanalytic terms, one might say that with Mesmer there were counter-transference problems. He seems to have attached great importance to the patient's convulsive crisis, while Puységur was "satisfied" with verbal com-

_____

*A similar view might be taken of the notion of "libido". Moreover, as Voutsinas remarks, one is no more entitled to reduce all Mesmer's discoveries to fluidism than to limit Freud's to the libido. The motives of the opponents of Mesmer and of Freud have in common the factor of unconscious submission to sexual taboos. When Freud spoke openly of sexual problems, he was accused of pansexualism. Mesmer made no reference to them, but his opponents sensed that they were there. The members of the Royal Commission published, in 1784, in addition to the official report, a secret report referring to the sexual peculiarities of magnetized patients(181).

munication (cf. 177). It must be emphasized, moreover, that the "crisis", in one form or another, not necessarily convulsive, has long been known as a turning-point in an illness, with a beneficial effect. The cathartic method used since Janet and Breuer also involves the idea of crisis. It may well be that the idea of an intense emotional turmoil and of a painful period on the way to cure (which has been interpreted by some as a form of expiation) has left its mark on Freud's explanation of the therapeutic process of psychoanalysis. He writes, "... it is contrary to all our beliefs about energy in general that a minimum exertion should be able to remove a heavy load by approaching it directly without the assistance of any suitably-devised appliance. In so far as the circumstances are at all comparable, experience shows that this trick cannot be performed successfully with the neuroses" (84, pp. 376–7). Thus Freud thinks that hypnotic therapy, which is relatively superficial, "works cosmetically", analytic therapy "surgically" (*ibid.*).

The fate of animal magnetism and the verdict of the Academies in 1784 are well known (179, 180).* These bodies made a very conscientious study, describing a number of hypnotic phenomena, and even acknowledged some curative aspects. In attributing these to imagination, they felt that they were condemning Mesmer's animal magnetism. "Imagination without magnetism can produce convulsions... Magnetism without imagination has no effect at all" (180, p. 64). D'Eslon (61, p. 47) had already, in 1780, very sensibly remarked, "If the medicine of imagination is the best, why should we not practise the medicine of imagination?"† This is regarded by some as the beginning of psychotherapy. The battle was joined forthwith. At first, during the first half of the nineteenth century, the issue was between the "fluidists" and the "animists". Later, it was between the proponents of physiological explanation and those of psychological explanation. Braid (30) was conclusively to refute the fluidist theory and, in order to emphasize his opposition to it, to apply the term

---

*The famous Report of the Commissioners appointed by the King (180) is also known as the Bailly report, the famous astronomer having been chairman. Among the signatories of this Report are Bailly, B. Franklin, Guillotin and Lavoisier. The comments made by the committees of the Academies are based upon the examination of D'Eslon's patients. Mesmer protested against this and proposed a scientifically rigorous procedure, the use of control groups. He wanted a study to be made of twenty-four patients treated by his method and an equal number treated by the customary methods of the time; but his proposal was not adopted.

†It is interesting to observe that Paracelsus (1490–1541), viewed as a precursor of the theory of animal magnetism taken up by Mesmer, had already admitted the "psychological" or "interpersonal" side of "magnetic" phenomena. "Without imagination and faith," he used to say of these, "no results can be achieved," and again, "Whether the object of belief be real or imaginary, the results will be the same."

"hypnotism" to the phenomena previously referred to by the name of "animal magnetism". He advanced a neuro-physiological theory of hypnosis, according to which hypnosis is induced by visual fixation,* and later added verbal suggestion. But to Liébeault (135) is due the credit for having been the first to use verbal suggestion systematically and on a large scale for therapeutic purposes.

Liébeault is also said to have been strongly "anti-fluidist", but this judgement may require to be qualified. From 1883, the date of publication of his pamphlet *Étude sur le Zoomagnetisme* (136), Liébeault held that hypnotic effects might be due either to psychological influence or to "the direct nervous effect of one man upon another". This work is very little known and seems even to have escaped the attention of Janet, who makes no mention of it in his *Psychological Healing* (105). We ourselves consulted it in the course of our bibliographic researches on animal hypnosis, believing, from the title, that it had to do with our subject. But for Liébeault, zoomagnetism is the equivalent of animal magnetism, in other words human hypnosis. It is worth while giving an account of this historical curiosity. In it Liébeault describes how he moved from a definite anti-fluidist position to a point of view accepting the direct effect of one organism on another, parallel to the psychological influence. In 1868, after having practised hypnosis for eight years, he began to have his first doubts. He had been struck by a remark of Dupotet, a well-known magnetizer of the time, to the effect that any sleeping child could be magnetized by passes. In 1880, he decided to experiment himself on wide-awake children suffering from diarrhoea, vomiting, anorexia, bronchitis, whooping-cough and the like. He reports forty-five cases, of which thirty-two were between two months and three years of age. Results were satisfactory. His procedures consisted of touching without pressure and there was no verbal suggestion (Liébeault, in any case, believed such suggestion to be ineffective with children of less than three years of age). He thus interpreted his success as being due to "zoomagnetism or neurility exercised by one living creature upon another" (136, p. 5). He then asked whether *anyone* could "touch", and answered in the negative, arguing that the children had been for hours in their mothers' arms without getting any better. He advanced the hypothesis that the only people who could "touch" effectively were "men with a well-developed nervous system or strong combustions of blood". Liébeault defined his position as follows. "Although I have been a psychological magnetist and have for long opposed the fluidist theory, I can no longer regard certain phenomena as not being due to the effect of one organism on another, without any interference with the conscious thinking of the subject concerned. There are elements of truth to be found in both camps, and it is time we stopped accusing each other of being misled by imaginary beliefs, and came to an agreement" (op. cit., p. 4).

What view can be taken today of the observations reported by Liébeault? It must be admitted that they lack scientific rigour; there is, for example, no control group to confirm one's confidence in the results. These results, however, can be rendered somewhat more comprehensible by modern psychosomatics. Most of the disorders of the children observed are of what would now be called a

---

*This technique was already employed by Mesmer, but he did not regard it as an inducing factor.

psychosomatic nature, and the close dependence of such symptoms upon the mother's anxiety is well known. The positive results reported might in some cases be due to the contacts of the therapist with the mother having implicit psychotherapeutic effects, as a result of which the child's symptoms disappeared. (It is well known that some feeding difficulties, such as vomiting, anorexia and the like, frequently disappear after the mother has psychotherapy.)

Later, Liébeault actually used "magnetized" water (1884). But shortly after this, at Bernheim's instigation, he gave "pseudo-magnetized" water (placebo effect), obtained identical results, once more admitted the importance of suggestion and abjured his fluidist faith, in the work which appeared in 1891 (137). It seems that Liébeault was not yet, however, definitely committed, although, to our knowledge, after this date he did not affirm a change of opinion in writing. However, in 1900 at the age of 77 he agreed to be honorary president of the Société d'Études Psychiques de l'Est whose members definitely believed in the existence of a fluid. Bernheim himself in a lecture which he gave in 1906, two years after Liébeault's death, recognized that Liébeault, "in spite of his psychological outlook . . . did not completely reject the 'fluidist' effects" (21).

Liébeault's vacillation appears to be due to the lack at that time of modern psychosomatic ideas. But it may also be explained in terms of the irrational motives which often determine scientific orientation. We shall return to these questions in a future work.

Whereas indeed Liébeault gave most of his attention to the role of the psychological factors in hypnosis, Charcot devoted himself mainly to the study of the physiological factors. Of this, Janet wrote, "He (Charcot) undoubtedly realized that peculiar and extremely important psychological phenomena were involved in these states; he was familiar with suggestion, discussed it and, if the occasion arose, would use it. But he repeated again and again that these psychological phenomena were very complex and difficult to study . . ." (105, I, p. 151).

At this time people wanted a clear-cut clinical picture, with unambiguous indications. The end of the nineteenth century in fact coincides with the triumph of positivistic thinking, reflected in medicine by the domination of the atomistic, Virchowian approach. To the physician, the psychological point of view did not seem to offer any dependable guides. But this is perhaps not enough to explain the intensity of the opposition to the psychological point of view which then developed. Unconscious factors, of the kind which always enter into the picture when psychotherapeutic questions are involved, must be assumed to have been at work.

To illustrate this opposition to the psychological theory, we might profitably refer to the study of metalloscopy, a very peculiar chapter in medical history, and one which certainly

deserves a more thorough study. In any case, it was through
metalloscopy that Charcot came to study hypnosis. It is amazing
that at the time we are talking of, the very existence of suggestion
was denied while reputable physicians experimented with
metalloscopy, metallotherapy, the transfer of symptoms by
magnets and the effects of drugs at a distance.

The effects of metals on hysterics was "discovered" by Burq (40) about 1850.
He had observed that a somnambulist touching a brass button fell down in a
cataleptic fit. This phenomenon did not occur when the button was protected
by a glove. Burq studied metalloscopy for twenty-five years and in 1876 he ap-
proached Claude Bernard, then president of the Société de Biologie, who appointed a committee (composed of Charcot, Luys and Dumontpallier) to verify
the facts reported by Burq. This committee experimented for a year in Charcot's
department on hysterics and presented a report confirming Burq's discovery.
"The researches in metalloscopy", said Dumontpallier at the Congress of
Hypnotism in 1889, "were to lead the members of this committee to study the
effects of electricity, electro-magnets, magnetized iron and the various procedures used by the magnetizers to produce somnambulism, catalepsy and
lethargy." "Expectant attention and suggestion have no part in certain determinants of hypnotism", added Dumontpallier. It was physical factors which
were the determinants of hypnosis — light, temperature, the vibrations in the
atmosphere, electricity and magnets. All these factors brought about "modifications of the nervous system" (52, p. 109).

The Salpêtrière school, with Charcot, saw hypnosis as a
pathological state, an artificial hysterical neurosis. Although he
regarded hysteria as a mental illness, Charcot made no attempt to
study the psychological factors in hypnosis in any detail. On the
other hand, the Nancy school, whose most important figures
were Bernheim, Liébeault, Beaunis and Liégeois, believed it to
be a normal psychological phenomenon. The controversy between
the two schools was very bitter.* It is perhaps of interest to note
in passing that men like Janet and Freud at first defended the
Salpêtrière school. Janet spoke after Bernheim at the Congress
of Hypnotism in 1889. "Even if I look at things from a purely
psychological point of view," he said, "I believe that M. Bernheim has expressed dangerous opinions which might lead to
the suppression of any kind of determinism. For my own part,
I do not hesitate to say that his interpretations are also anti-
psychological, for psychology, like physiology, has its laws,
the operation of which cannot be interfered with by suggestion"
(52, p. 109). Freud, in his preface to Bernheim's book in 1888,

*A detailed account of this controversy is to be found in Cuvellier's disserta-
tion (58).

likewise defends the Salpêtrière school. What troubles him is that if we admit that suggestion can produce all the hypnotic phenomena, then it should equally produce hysteria, and this Freud will not admit. Ferenczi (76) later attempted to reconcile the views of the two schools by showing the truth-content of both theories. This he did by adopting the concept of the Freudian transference in order to understand the hypnotic relationship. The symptoms of hysteria, like hypnotic phenomena, occur as a function of the emotions experienced by the subject in relation to a significant figure in one's past in the case of hysteria, and represented by the hypnotist in the case of hypnotic phenomena.

The victory of the Nancy school was recognized outside France. Among others, the Pavlovian school admitted the importance of suggestion and interpersonal "rapport" though they did not study them at the level of depth psychology. They were content to define suggestion in physiological terms.

Thus Nicolaiev (162), using language somewhat reminiscent of that of Dumont-pallier, wrote in 1927 that hypnosis was brought about by stimulation by physical agents* which he classified in hierarchical order. The most effective of these were thermal stimuli, and then came tactile stimuli and then auditory stimuli. The Russian authors actually employed "passes", giving them a physiological interpretation. They were tactile stimuli (Pavlov) or thermal stimuli (Nicolaiev). They also introduced luminous passes which for some subjects acted as visual stimuli (Ivanov-Smolenski) and for some as thermal stimuli (Nicolaiev). It may be remarked in passing that some American authors (Klemperer, 116) express themselves in favour of passes, which they interpret in a psychodynamic framework, the stroking of the forehead encouraging sleep by evoking infantile reminiscences.

It will be recalled that Charcot (1878–82) convinced the Academies of the reality of hypnotic phenomena and that these became the object of researches. This respect for hypnosis did not survive Charcot's death. The study of hypnosis was abandoned in France. Elsewhere the decline was less obvious. There was a revival of interest in hypnosis after the First World War, but even today doctors show a certain reluctance, and have continually to be convinced of the reality of hypnosis. In the series of reports of learned societies which mark the history of hypnosis, is that of the British Medical Association in 1955, which officially rehabilitated hypnosis in Great Britain (186). In 1958, the

---

*We shall see later (cf. p. 30ff.) that recent theories of hypnosis deriving from egopsychology and the work on "sensory deprivation" re-emphasize, in a different perspective, the importance of the physical factor in the induction and explanation of hypnosis.

American Medical Association integrated hypnosis into medical therapeutics, defining the conditions for its use (187). The most recent statement at the present time (1961) is that of the American Psychiatric Association (183), in which it is said, "Hypnosis is a specialized psychiatric procedure and as such is an aspect of doctor-patient relationship. Hypnosis provides an adjunct to research, to diagnosis and to treatment in psychiatric practice. It is also of some value in other areas of medical practice and research."

It is interesting to note that the committee set up by the British Medical Association deliberately based itself on the report made to the Académie Royale de Médecine by Husson in 1831. The members of the committee affirmed that its "conclusions... showed remarkable foresight and are mainly applicable today."*
This simply emphasizes that, in 130 years, progress in the field of hypnosis has been remarkably slow compared, for example, with that of physics, not to mention astronautics ...

In France, the disaffection was complete. After the last works published by Janet, which date from 1919, and with the exception of an article by Parcheminey already referred to, there was silence on the subject. Doubtless some isolated workers still sometimes used hypnosis in semi-secrecy.† But the general atmosphere was one of hostility, particularly obvious in Babinski's‡ old pupils. On the one hand, critics went so far as to deny the very existence of hypnosis, while on the other hand they accused it of being ineffective and dangerous and regarded it as a mixture of trick, fraud and pretence.§

It is well known that the Nancy school of hypnology began to decline from the moment when it attached more importance to suggestion than to hypnosis. Everything became just suggestion. Thus a well-intentioned pharmacist, Coué, regarded himself as continuing the work of this school when he introduced the famous auto-

---

*Husson's report was received with reserve by the Academy, led to no public discussion and was not printed.

†Berillon, whose name recalls the flourishing period of hypnosis (he was the general secretary of the 1889 Congress and editor of the *Revue de l'Hypnotisme*) had, until his death in 1948, been practising hypnotherapy according to the ideas dating from the end of the previous century.

‡A psychobiographical study of Babinski might one day reveal unconscious emotional problems in relation to his master Charcot. Certainly, although he was a great neurologist and a distinguished researcher, Babinski lacked the genial intuition of his master in sensing the psychological problems involved in the genesis of certain pathological manifestations (7).

§This attitude is still to be found in our own time, as is shown by the views expressed by a psychiatrist in a generally very courteous review of the previous edition of this book. He took the view that hypnosis is ineffective and involves fraud, and proposed that the old debate on this subject should be renewed. (*Ann. méd.-psychol.*, 1962, 120, I, 1, p. 190.)

suggestion, which rather unexpectedly attracted world-wide interest, although on Coué's death in 1926 the popularity of his method began to wane.

During the thirties, another pharmacist, Brotteaux (37), tried to use hypnosis through chemotherapy (cf. p. 126). He obtained a hypnotic state by means of the drug scopochloralose, after which he gave therapeutic suggestions. "The hypnosis of Liébeault, Richet, Janet and others", he wrote, "will be rehabilitated, thanks to a more effective and more scientific method of hypnotizing" (38). This procedure was to replace the "torpillage" of hysterics by faradic currents which was used in hospitals (and still is, along with the amphetamine shock therapy introduced after the last war). However, the psychiatrists (Baruk and his followers) who took up Brotteaux's work completely ignored its psychological and interpersonal aspect. They did not consider the state of consciousness created by the drug, believing in the direct chemical action of the drug on the hysterical disorder.

A slow rehabilitation of hypnosis has been taking place during the past decade. In January 1951 Bachet and Padovani (8) presented a paper to the Société Médico-psychologique on the treatment of pain in amputees by "non-verbal suggestion". By simply looking the patients in the eyes, they obtained a "light cataleptiform trance-state and sometimes sleep." In a second paper in November of the same year, Bachet (9) maintains that the state obtained by his treatment is "an inhibitory state of a hypnotic type", of which he gives a Pavlovian explanation. What is involved is, apparently, a hypnotic state, but Bachet avoids any kind of verbal suggestion in order to remain – as he was to explain later (9) – on a more scientific level, nearer to animal experimentation. In January 1953, the present writer, with Montassut and Gachkel (154) gave a paper to the Société Médico-psychologique on the classic use of hypnosis and verbal suggestion.* It was concerned with the treatment by suggestion under hypnosis (in 1949) of a hysterical amnesia. Also in 1953 there appeared another study by two psychiatrists (73); and the following year, an anaesthesiologist published a work on the application of hypnosis in his field (129). Finally, the year 1953 also saw the emergence of a technique derived from hypnosis, the Autogenic Training of J. H. Schultz (2). Its progress has run parallel to the development of hypnosis in in other countries. Although Autogenic Training had its roots in hypnosis, it escaped the taboo which afflicted the latter.

In 1955 appeared the volume on Psychiatry in the *Encyclopédie Médico-Chirurgicale*, with a chapter devoted to hypnosis. The chapter occupies only seven pages, although techniques of relaxation take eight and narco-analysis ten. This indicates how little interest there is in France in hypnosis. The number of French works remains extremely limited. In a bibliographical study of the period 1955–60, Montserrat-Estève (155) lists 505 titles on hypnosis. Of this number only nine are by French authors.

---

*The last paper on hypnosis given at this society dates back to 1889. It was read by Chambard under the title of *Remarks on the dangers of experimental hypnotism and suggestion. (Ann. méd.-psychol.,* 1889, 47, I, 292–301, session of January 1889.)

Theories of Hypnosis

IT IS difficult to find a satisfactory definition of hypnotism or hypnosis. These two terms have very similar meanings. The former was first used by Braid in 1843 and introduced into France a few years later. Littré in 1863 defines it in his dictionary as follows: "*Hypnotism:* physiological term. A kind of magnetic state induced by making someone look at a bright object held near the eyes."

It is difficult to say just when the word "hypnosis" appeared. The *Grand Dictionnaire universel Larousse* gives it for the first time in the 1865–90 edition (vol. IX, H–K, 1873) with the following definition: "Sleep induced especially by prolonged fixation of bright objects."

We make no distinction between the two terms, although it must be pointed out that some writers do, regarding "hypnosis" as a state, and "hypnotism" as a collection of techniques for producing this state.

Certain Spanish authors have recently proposed a change in terminology and would like to replace the words "hypnosis" and "hypnotherapy" by "sophrose" and "sophrotherapy" respectively, with a view to getting rid of the magical connotation of the word "hypnosis". But this seems to us scarcely justified. The terms proposed do not indicate any theoretical change, as was the case when Braid replaced "animal magnetism" by "hypnotism". And it may well be that the halo of mystery which surrounds the word "hypnosis" constitutes a motivational factor which facilitates at the outset the establishment of the psychotherapeutic relationship. This magical quality can disappear later. It also, however, seems possible that some medical men refuse to establish any relationship with their patients on these terms, and this may be the real unconscious motive of those who advocate the change in terminology. Furthermore, it is quite likely, as the well-known social psychologist Otto Klineberg has pointed out to the writer, that if this change in terminology was adopted, the new word would eventually take on exactly the same meaning as the old, since the technique itself would remain unchanged.

To return to modern literature, Porot's (173) *Manuel alphabétique de Psychiatrie* (in 1952) gives the following definition: "The name *hypnosis* is given to a state of incomplete sleep of a special, artificially induced kind."

The definition proposed by the committee of the British Medical

Association is more elaborate. It states that hypnosis is: "a temporary condition of altered attention in the subject which may be induced by another person and in which a variety of phenomena may appear spontaneously or in response to verbal or other stimuli. These phenomena include alterations in consciousness and memory, increased susceptibility to suggestion and the production in the subject of responses and ideas unfamiliar to him in his usual state of mind. Further, phenomena such as anaesthesia, paralysis and rigidity of muscles, and vasomotor changes can be produced and removed in the hypnotic state" (186, p. 191).

We need not multiply examples of the kinds of definition which we have quoted. None of them is adequate. Each one reflects its author's idea of the nature of the phenomenon, as we shall see later. Besides, the field of hypnosis is not clearly delimited and there are no objective criteria of the hypnotic state. We do not know what is due specifically to hypnosis and what is due to direct or indirect suggestion. In other words, we must ask whether there is anything specific to hypnosis over and above the factors introduced by the hypnotist.

Some writers have even expressed doubts about the very existence of hypnosis. But the fact that a phenomenon cannot be precisely defined does not mean that it has no existence of its own. One extreme of opinion is represented by those who consider that everything is due to suggestion. At the other extreme, there are some who favour the existence of a specific hypnotic state resting upon an almost physical basis; and from this point of view, the hypnotic state is compared to post-encephalitic states (196). The Pavlovian school likewise speak of a characteristic hypnotic state, a state of partial sleep. Schultz (201) also favours the existence of "pure hypnosis" (Heilschlaf); while for Kretschmer (120), hypnosis can actually be separated into "its constituent neurophysiological and psychophysiological mechanisms".

To emphasize the complexity of the problem, it should be stressed once more that the trance is a labile and dynamic state which changes from one session to the next according to the psychotherapeutic situation. Schilder (197) has already drawn attention to the fact that the depth of the trance, in the classic sense of the term, does not always correspond to the depth of involvement of the subject's personality in the hypnotic relationship.

A subject in a state of somnambulism may be less involved in the hypnotic relationship than another subject who is only in a light trance. The older authors had, of course, already claimed that the therapeutic effect of hypnosis did not always depend upon the depth of trance. Moreover, the trance may sometimes depend more upon the psychological aspects and sometimes more upon the physiological. According to his own personality, the subject will mobilize more physiological or more psychological structures.

Some day—to put forward a highly speculative hypothesis—this perspective may be of use in elucidating the very difficult problem of why a subject chooses to express himself by a psychoneurosis or by a psychosomatic disorder. It might be that those who, in the interpersonal relationship, react more on the physiological level would tend toward psychosomatic disorder and those who react more on the psychological level would tend toward psychoneurosis.

Again, it is impossible to determine whether a subject is hypnotized or not. Some subjects believe themselves to have been hypnotized when in fact they have not been, while others think they have not been hypnotized when in fact they have been. There may also be, as Kubie (124) has remarked, conscious, preconscious or unconscious simulation. Yet again, some subjects may derive therapeutic advantage from hypnosis because they really were in a trance, while others derive a similar benefit from not having allowed themselves to be hypnotized. The patient here gives up his symptom by way of resistance to the treatment. This kind of behaviour might almost be called "flight into recovery".

By way of example, consider the case of a man of sixty years of age who came from abroad to consult the present writer for a reactive depression. After the loss of his partner in life, he was afflicted with sadness, apathy and complete anorexia. He was convinced that hypnosis alone could cure him. On his arrival in Paris and before coming to see us, he consulted a former edition of the present book. This made him realize, as he was to tell us, that hypnotherapy was not the harmless treatment he had thought. At the same time, he felt his sadness growing less and, the same evening, he had his first square meal in several months. When he visited us the following day, he declared that he no longer needed a hypnotic session. A straightforward psychotherapeutic talk was enough to confirm his feeling of recovery.

Even an unsuccessful attempt at hypnosis activates psychodynamic currents and may mobilize defences to advantage. The writer treated a man of 55 years of age suffering from an anxiety depressive state with hypochondriac delusions. Several ill-advised surgical operations had aggravated the patient's condition and his attention was entirely concentrated upon his anal region. He went so far as to ask for an artificial anus to be provided. All kinds of treatment, including shock treatment and prolonged sleep treatment had proved ineffective. The patient had used massive doses of purgatives to deal with obstinate constipation; he had taken large quantities of drugs and alcohol to relieve his attacks of anxiety, and a toxic confusional state had actually resulted. Hypnotic therapy remained. The case was certainly not suitable for this form of therapy but in the face of the insistence of the attendant physician and the patient, we made experimentally several attempts at hypnosis. The patient, of course, being very narcissistic, was resistant, but this resistance to interpersonal involvement gave rise to a defensive process which in turn resulted in a slight remission of symptoms. The patient was able to resume work for a fortnight, and broke off treatment, concluding—with mixed regret and triumph—that he could not be "magnetized".

There are no comprehensive theories explaining hypnosis. All the theories are partial theories. In general there are three main theoretical trends. (1) The first is based upon the Pavlovian school. (2) The second is inspired by experimental psychology. (3) The third is derived from psychoanalysis. We shall devote some attention to these three trends, spend some time on the relations between hypnosis and sleep, and consider the question of animal hypnosis.

Pavlovian Theory

THE theory of hypnosis developed by the Pavlovian school is based on animal experiments. Birman (23) was able to establish experimentally a "waking zone" in a dog conditioned to the sound of a buzzer as a signal for food. When asleep, the dog would wake up for food only at the sound of the buzzer, remaining insensible to other sounds, even although these were more intense. The cortex of the dog was inhibited, with continuance of waking points in certain zones which remained responsive. This is the basis of the Pavlovian school's theory of hypnosis as partial sleep, a theory foreshadowed last century by Liébeault (135), Beaunis (18) and Brown-Séquart (39). According to this view, hypnosis is a state intermediary between waking and sleep, a state of partial sleep or partial inhibition,* partial just as much in respect of topography as in respect of intensity. Waking zones remain in the cortex which, in man, allow "rapport" between subject and hypnotist.

Hypnosis includes three phases called "hypnoidal phases" — the "phase of equalization", the "paradoxical" phase and the "ultra-paradoxical" phase. In the phase of equalization, all conditioned stimuli, strong or weak, act in a similar way. In the paradoxical phase, a strong stimulus provokes a weak reaction or no reaction at all, while a weak stimulus provokes a strong reaction. In the ultra-paradoxical phase, a reaction may be obtained to a "negative stimulus", i.e., a stimulus to which the cerebral cells do not react in the wakeful state. The Pavlovian school think in these terms of the hypnotic phenomena obtained in the paradoxical phase, which Pavlov refers to as the "suggestive phase".

Platonov (172), interpreting Pavlov, explains that the "phasic states" are transitory and fleeting in normal physiological conditions, but can persist for weeks or even months in pathological

---

*A Soviet author (207, p. 154) has written recently (1962), "In explaining hypnosis (and sleep) by inhibition, we are bound to admit that so far we do not quite know just what this 'wretched phenomenon', to use Pavlov's expression, is."

conditions. The hypnoidal phases may be regarded, on the one hand as forming the physiological substratum of neuroses or psychoses; but on the other hand, they constitute "a normal form of the struggle against a morbid agent".

The application of these theories to man presents difficulties owing to the intervention of language, which the Pavlovians call the second signalling system. Speech becomes a signal, a "stimulus" just as "material" as any physical stimulus. But Pavlov continually emphasizes that these two kinds of stimulus cannot be compared either quantitatively or qualitatively, because of the existence of past experience in man. This is precisely where the difficulties arise, for the Pavlovian school have no room for unconscious layers in the past emotional experience of the subject. Moreover, interpersonal communication does not take place only on the verbal level.

At the famous joint meeting of the two Academies of the Sciences and Medicine in the U.S.S.R. in 1950 (149), which gave official approval to the primacy of Pavlovian physiology in medicine, a number of speakers (Birman, Giliarovski, Popov, Platonov, Streltchouk and Ivanov-Smolenski) recommended the study and use of hypnosis,* which was regarded as a form of psychotherapy with a physiological basis. Psychology started to be rehabilitated in 1956, and is gradually freeing itself from the domination of physiology. This rehabilitation was marked by the appearance in *Kommounist* (March 1956, no. 4, pp. 87–93), of an editorial article entitled *On bridging the gap between theory and practice in psychology*. An important meeting attended by a thousand scientists was held in Moscow from 8th to 12th May 1962, arranged by the Academies of Science, Medicine and Education (summarized in Korsakov, *J. Neurol. Psychiat.*, 1962, **62**, 10, 1578–82). This conference was on "philosophical problems of higher nervous activity and psychology". It attacked certain dogmatic interpretations of the decisions of the 1950 conference and officially rehabilitated psychology, raising it to the status of an autonomous science.

Authors are to be found emphasizing that the Pavlovian theory does not provide a complete explanation of hypnosis. Horvai, a Czechoslovakian investigator with a Pavlovian orientation,

---

*This indicates the change in the attitude of the Academies since 1784.

wrote in 1959, "The Pavlovian theory of hypnosis is not a dogma. Pavlov's ideas were not sufficiently elaborated ... some are no more than hypotheses" (98, p. 37). According to Horvai, these ideas should all be treated as starting points for new research. For the application of Pavlovian theory to hypnotic psychotherapy Boul (27), Horvai (98), Konstoroum (119), Lebedinski (132), Platonov (172), Rojnov (190), Slobodniak (207), Sviadoshtsh (215) and Volgyesi (227) should be consulted. The article by Svorad and Hoskovec (217) contains an important bibliography of clinical and experimental studies of hypnosis in the Soviet Union and East European countries.

Theories Inspired by Experimental Psychology

THE authors included in this chapter are too numerous for us to be able to summarize all their work. Thus, we shall unfortunately be unable to give a detailed account of the theories of Hull (99), White (234, 235), Sarbin (194), Weitzenhoffer (230), and others. The interested reader should refer to the writings of these authors or to the account of them given by Frank A. Pattie (167) in the book by Dorcus (63).

The work on hypnosis of Hull, the first of the authors mentioned above, is in a tradition of research which goes back to Bernheim. Bernheim, discouraged by his bitter struggle with the Salpêtrière school and at variance with Liébeault, had finally stated dogmatically, "There is no such thing as hypnotism, there is only suggestibility." Hull, influenced as he was by behaviourism, applied himself (1933) to the study of suggestibility as a single dimension. The effect of suggestibility is, according to Hull, to keep the "symbolic processes" of the subject in a state of passivity, and to allow the "symbolic stimulation" conveyed to him by the experimenter to lead to action. This comes very close to what Bernheim called "the law of ideo-dynamism" according to which, in certain conditions, the idea can be directly transformed into movement. Bernheim had concluded that suggestibility was the process by which the brain "accepts the idea and transforms it into action" (20, p. 203).

With White (1941), there is a marked change in perspective in that the motivational point of view is introduced. He defines hypnotic behaviour as "meaningful, goal-directed striving, its most general goal being to behave like a hypnotized person as this is continuously defined by the operator and understood by the subject" (234).

Sarbin (1950) emphasizes the importance of "role-taking" in the behaviour of the hypnotized subject, "role-taking" being for him a general form of socio-psychological behaviour of which hypnosis is a particular case.

19

The ideas of White and Sarbin have recently been taken up again and considerably enriched by Orne (164, 165). Orne was struck by the fact that the attitude of subjects under hypnosis had always been, at different periods, related to current ideas about hypnosis. By way of example, he cites two extremes. In Mesmer's sessions, the patients, without any verbal suggestion, went into convulsive "crises". On the other hand, the subjects who applied Coué's method (regarded by Orne as a kind of hypnotic technique) never showed any overt sign of a trance state. Orne accordingly asked whether hypnosis did really have some specific basis, or whether it was entirely a socio-cultural product. In order to show the effect of prior knowledge, he conducted the following experiment.

During a course on hypnosis, he indicated to his students that catalepsy of the dominant hand was one of the characteristic phenomena associated with hypnotic state. (In fact, this is not so, catalepsy normally affecting *both* hands, but the assertion appeared plausible.) At the same time, the students were present at a hypnotic session during which the subjects actually manifested catalepsy of the dominant hand, having been instructed previously to behave in this way. These same students, then themselves hypnotized, also showed catalepsy of the dominant hand.*

In this example, the subject received from the hypnotist precise though indirect cues to how to behave. But the problem of knowing how much of the subject's attitude derives from the experimenter is sometimes very difficult, for what the experimenter expects of the subject may be communicated to the subject unconsciously. Under the heading of "demand characteristics of the experimental situation", Orne includes all the signs indicating the intentions or desires of the hypnotist, including the implicit and non-verbal indications emanating from the experimenter and the indications yielded by the experimental procedure. However, the "demand characteristics of the experimental situation" are not experienced only by the subject, but also by the experimenter. Hypnosis may, in many ways, be considered as a case of *folie à deux,* each of the members involved in the hypnotic relationship playing the role which the

---

*Catalepsy, as used here, refers to the fact that if the experimenter raises the subject's hand, it remains in this position.

other expects of him. The subject behaves as if he could not resist the suggestions of the hypnotist, while the latter plays the role of an omnipotent personage. Thus, not only does the subject experience a suggested hallucination, but the hypnotist also acts as if the subject were hallucinating.* This reciprocity of role of hypnotist and hypnotized was shown in a case in which the experimenter, on meeting his subject, was sure that he was a simulator. In actual fact, the subject was quite capable of going into a deep trance. But the session which followed was a failure; the subject was hostile to the hypnotist who, while giving the usual suggestions, was unable to play his complementary role in a convincing manner.

Brotteaux (38) had already laid much emphasis on unconscious communication between hypnotist and subject. He cites the work of a surgeon who used scopo-chloralose to supplement anaesthesia. For Brotteaux, the basic effect of this drug is hypersuggestibility. But the surgeon in question did not think so, for "in theory, he did not accept the use of hypnotism and suggestion; in fact, he said that the replacement of the patient's own will by that of another was the most serious crime that a human being could commit against his fellow-men". Brotteaux goes on to add, "It is the usual story in hypnotism, where one gets the subjects one wants . . . Liégeois and Liébeault had perfectly docile subjects. Brouardel and Babinski could not get them to carry out suggestions which they thought should conflict with their moral feelings. Fundamentally, in all cases, the subjects carry out the suggestions which basically correspond to the hypnotist's preconceived ideas . . . From the time of Charcot, it had been agreed that hysterics should show spectacular nervous manifestations . . . Then came Babinski, who did not believe in the reality of these attacks . . . and of course found none; although unaware of the fact, he suggested to his patients that they should no longer show these particular signs of their illness."

Orne thinks that it is difficult to determine the behaviour which is characteristic of hypnosis *itself*, since there is practically no chance of finding naïve subjects entirely free from the influence of their socio-cultural environment. If a fundamental process could be uncovered beneath the many socio-cultural layers, this would be, for this author, the essential core of hypnosis.

According to Orne (164), socio-cultural factors play an extremely important part in all forms of psychotherapy, not only in hypnosis. The process which goes on during psychotherapy is conditioned by the ideas which patients and subjects

---

*This case does not, of course, represent a case of *folie à deux* in the usual sense of the term, for it lacks the quality of delusional conviction, not only on the part of the hypnotist, but also on the part of the subject, whose ego always retains a certain degree of control over reality, and can at any moment re-establish the situation. If Orne's expression were to be taken literally, it would delight certain present-day opponents of hypnosis in France, who like to quote Dupré's sardonic comment to the effect that one might question which was the more mad, the hypnotist or the subject.

have about it at any given time. For example, current ideas about the duration of a course of psychotherapy largely determine the progress of the treatment. The very effectiveness of treatment depends to some extent on the faith which members of the society have in it. Thus, in Orne's view, if we are to identify the essential core of the psychotherapeutic process in general, we must isolate it from all its sociocultural aspects.

It is certainly important to emphasize the influence of socio-cultural factors on the behaviour of the subject; but they do not seem to us to be so decisive as to Orne. They must come to terms with the psychobiological substratum. Different "patterns" may coexist. Thus, it is not true that at the end of the eighteenth century all hypnotized subjects had a convulsive seizure. Even round Mesmer's "baquet", all the patients were not always in a convulsive state. Some walked about and talked among themselves. There is plenty of evidence that this was so. We give only a few examples.

Mahon (1752–1801), an expert in forensic medicine and an historian of medicine (143), who was present at Mesmer's treatments, wrote in a pamphlet dated 31st July 1784, "I have seen men in a state recalling descriptions of somnambulists, with eyes open but fixed, not speaking, but showing by signs what they wanted, and seeming to hear what was said to them, relatively attentive to what they were doing... certain later to *remember nothing about what had happened*."* (post-hypnotic amnesia).

A Swiss theologian, Charles Moulinie (1757–1824) also reports (in a pamphlet dated 24th April 1784) that there was in Mesmer's entourage a young female domestic of 13 years of age who, when magnetized, behaved like a natural somnambulist (158).

The famous report by Bailly (dated 11th August 1784) also provides examples of quiet and even frankly somnambulistic behaviour. "... one is astonished by the deep relaxation of some of these patients ... One can see patients who seek one another out in an exclusive way and, hurrying to one another, speak in a kindly manner to one another and lessen the severity of one another's crisis." (180, p. 7).

An anonymous author (182) who was present at Mesmer's experiments reports (3rd September 1784) that he had seen somnambulists indicating the seat of trouble in other magnetized members of the group (it is well known that "diagnostic ability" was recognized at this time as a characteristic of somnambulists).

The report (dated 12th September 1784) of the celebrated botanist de Jussieu, the dissident member of the commission of the Royal Society of Medicine, mentions the case of a young man who "wandered peacefully about the room, and often touched the patients ... When he returned to his normal state, he spoke, could remember nothing of what had happened, and could no longer magnetize. I drew no conclusion from this, which was repeated several times before my eyes" (110, p. 10).

Again, Aubin-Gautier reports the case of Marguerite, a young woman of 25 who, when magnetized by Mesmer's assistant Dr. Aubry,† frequently became

---

* Our italics.

†Mesmer had two treatment rooms, one for the rich, the other for the poor. The latter were treated by the master himself, while the assistant looked after the wealthy patients.

somnambulistic. One day, when she had been magnetized in Dr. Aubry's absence, no one could awaken her properly and she had to go to Dr. Aubry's house to be "demagnetized" (86, II, p. 247).

About the same time, Puységur magnetized the famous shepherd Victor, without his showing any violent motor reaction. It is impossible in the circumstances to claim that Victor was role-playing. Pattie, reminding us that de Jussieu was the first to come upon "post-magnetic amnesia", took a similar view, observing that "this amnesia, previously unknown, could not have been part of a role at the time" (63, I, p. 28). (The amnesia in question, as we have indicated, had already been reported before de Jussieu, but that in no way alters the problem.)

If violent "crises" were not the inevitable rule in the Mesmerian period, they were not its particular prerogative either, for they still occur in the hypnosis of clearly hysterical personalities. It is plausible that Mesmer's first patient was a hysteric. Since he felt satisfied with this pattern, because of countertransference and also on rational grounds (since the "crisis" itself is a salutary conclusion), Mesmer fastened on to it and later his subjects adopted it by imitation. The master regarded somnambulism as an undesirable secondary effect of the magnetic state; our view, on the contrary, is that the convulsive crisis represented a hysterical exaggeration of this state. It would appear that the whole range of hypnotic phenomena already existed in the "magnetic" state of the Mesmer period. This problem is, however, very complex, since it is difficult to disentangle what is genuine from what is (consciously or unconsciously) simulated. It is interesting to note that the older authors were already aware of this aspect of the problem. In the "secret report"* (181), we find the following observation. "There is another way in which these convulsions might be induced, of which the commissioners had no direct and positive proof, but which they could not but suspect; that is, a *simulated*† crisis which gave the signal for, or determined the occurrence of, many others by imitation." Charles de Villers wrote in 1787, "I believe that imagination‡ plays a big part in magnetism (and this is nothing against it, for *I am only recognizing a mental element*).§ Assuredly the first somnambulism was not the effect of imagination,

---

*A "secret report" was presented to the King at the same time as the public Bailly report.   †Italics in the original.

‡If we examine present-day usage of the word "imagination", we find that it is used in two senses, referring to two different levels of personality. Sometimes it refers to the inner emotional life with all its psychoaffective complexities, sometimes to the intellectual aspect of the individual in his "cultural" activities (learning, imitation and so on).   §Our italics.

but once this effect became known, a somnambulistic patient would find it very easy to fall into a similar state by the action of his mind alone, being well apprised that the tree or 'baquet' was going to produce this effect in him. But I am convinced that these somnambulists are not the genuine article." In our view, there may well be various kinds of somnambulism, at one extreme a genuine, "essential" type, representing a form of psychobiologically adaptive behaviour, at the other extreme a relatively superficial type "learned" by imitation, and in between a whole range of intermediary types. If this is so, the experience of Weitzenhoffer (232) who after several years of experimenting with hundreds of subjects had encountered barely a dozen genuine somnambulists, is not surprising. We have no statistical data of our own, and our experimental material is different, being provided mainly by "patients" and not by normal subjects like the students so widely used by experimenters in the United States, but we are well aware that "good subjects" are rare. It may be of some interest to emphasize that our best cases were subjects presenting spontaneous somnambulism or the phenomenon of multiple personality. Judging from published reports by the older authors, it would appear that in those days there were more somnambulists. It is difficult to say whether this is really so; but if we accept it, we must ask what the proportions of "genuine" and "imitation" were among them. If the former were more frequent than today (and this seems likely), we must admit that the "pattern" of behavioural expression has changed. This is true of hysteria. Even today in some developing countries, we find patterns of pathological behaviour which have disappeared in the more highly developed countries. This brings us back to the socio-cultural dimension which Orne has so vigorously emphasized. There is unquestionably much of interest in his research. But we have expressed some reservations on the rather extreme character of his hypotheses, as for example, his view that "naïve" subjects are scarcely to be found any more, which seems to us to be over-stating the case.

In France, where hypnosis is today in eclipse, it is not unusual to come upon patients who have no previous knowledge of hypnosis. Although they are left in ignorance of the nature of the psychotherapeutic treatment which they are given, their reaction is no different from that of other patients. Since it is difficult to see how it could be entirely determined by the hypnotist, we must assume the existence of a specific basis capable of supporting many variations. This basis appears in an elementary form in animal hypnosis. Animal hypnosis represents a form of adaptive behaviour consequent upon a change in the animal's relations with its surroundings and is characterized by the inhibition of motor activity (cf. p. 46). In man, the first stage in hypnosis also involves the suspension of activity of the motor system, the mechanism for reality testing. It may be objected that the somnambulist walks. But this is because, in man, psychodynamic phenomena enter the picture and the hypnotized subject may be said to walk, not by his own choice, but because the hypnotist wills him to.

The work of Barber (12) is again in the tradition of Bernheim. Barber, like Bernheim, tries to show that all so-called hypnotic phenomena—i.e., changes under hypnosis in the functioning of various physiological systems (sensory, circulatory, gastrointestinal, etc.)—could be produced by suggestion in predisposed subjects in the waking state.

This assimilation of hypnosis to suggestibility raises a problem to which we shall return later. Here, we shall merely observe that the proponents of this point of view nevertheless continue to use the techniques of instruction to produce phenomena for which, logically, suggestion should be enough. Bernheim himself had shown this same inconsistency.

Barber's work is undoubtedly of interest. In our view it shows the importance of interpersonal factors in the production of psychophysiological changes, in the waking state. But it must be emphasized that it does not contribute to our understanding of hypnosis. Hypnotic induction which involves manipulation on the sensory-motor and emotional level brings about a modification of the state of consciousness together with a particular intersubjective experience (which some regard as regressive). In most cases, hypersuggestibility is manifest though certain psychodynamic constellations may prevent its appearance. But when it does appear, it may allow effects to be achieved which are certainly deeper than those produced by suggestion in the waking state. A major surgical operation such as laparotomy is an example of the possible achievements of hypnosis which are not to be found in Barber's experiments. An attempt to do this kind of thing gave rise to the heart-rending spectacle provided by French television in a famous broadcast (in February 1963). A man "conditioned" but not hypnotized, had his appendix removed and showed all the signs of extreme suffering.

Weitzenhoffer (230), to begin with, largely followed Bernheim and Hull, regarding everything in hypnosis as due to suggestibility. But he seems to have modified this point of view, and in a recent article (232) recognizes that hypnosis includes "something else". He adds that Bernheim himself, in fact, was never so dogmatic as he is supposed to have been, and admitted the existence of a "hypnotic state" which could not be entirely assimilated to suggestion. Weitzenhoffer considers that there is basically no contradiction between Bernheim's views in 1887, when he still distinguished between the two states, and his views in 1903, when he tended to ignore the distinction, and that Bernheim's position was essentially unchanged.

We ourselves consider that Bernheim's writings in 1903 do in fact indicate a change, but it is true that they are marked by a certain degree of ambiguity which Bernheim was never able to overcome, and which was to persist even later in those writings in which he denied in the most outspoken way the existence of a hypnotic state *sui generis,* independent of suggestibility. This ambiguity is even more marked in his last formulation of his ideas (in 1917, two years before his death). On the question of the so-called hypnotic phenomena, he wrote, "none of these phenomena is restricted in its appearance to a special so-called hypnotic state. They can all be induced in the waking state in subjects who have never been put to sleep and have never seen anyone else put to sleep. I have found that in suggestible subjects, one can produce by verbal suggestion, in the waking state, the very same manifestations — anaesthesia, hallucinations, compulsive actions etc. — as can be produced in them in a state of induced sleep. It is therefore not the induced sleep which creates the suggestibility. *A state of sleep and a hypnotic state or a state of suggestibility are thus not related states.** Accordingly, I feel justified in saying that *there is no such thing as hypnotism, there is only suggestibility*"† (21a, p. 46). In even more positive terms. Bernheim replies to the objection that his assertion is paradoxical and that

---

* Our italics.

† Author's italics.

the suggestibility to which he refers is just hypnotism in the wakeful state. "It would be more exact," he writes, "to say 'Hypnosis is suggestion in the sleeping state' " (p. 47). The ambiguity is obvious here, and becomes even more so when the author adds, "It is also necessary, as I have said, for the sleep to be incomplete." But what is this "incomplete sleep"? Is there really such a thing? If so, it is a "state" which cannot be only that of suggestibility. This impression of ambiguity is not removed when Bernheim tries to clarify his ideas. He goes on, "Sleep is not essential to obtain the phenomena of suggestibility. These phenomena could have been discovered directly in the waking state, without the unnecessary intermediate state of induced sleep, and in this case the word *hypnotism* would never have been invented. The idea of a special magnetic or hypnotic state would not be attached to these phenomena. Suggestion is the child of the old hypnotism, just as chemistry is the child of alchemy" (p. 47). It can be seen from this that even in Bernheim's most positive statements there is an element of contradiction — there is a state, called by Bernheim (and others) "incomplete sleep" or "induced sleep" which is "something else" than pure suggestibility. It is just this "something else", this "incomplete sleep" which remains indefinable but which has existed for centuries and the study of which has produced so much passionate controversy.

This element of contradiction in Bernheim's theory, which we have just discussed above, suggests the hypothesis that the complete identity of hypnosis and suggestibility was unconsciously not entirely accepted by Bernheim himself, and that the progressively more positive stand which he took against hypnosis did not necessarily correspond to a very deep conviction. It would appear that Bernheim's successive positions were partly motivated by the battles which he had to fight on two fronts. On the one hand, there were the attacks of the Salpêtrière school, which, after Charcot's death and the defeat of the somatic theory of hypnosis, had finally denied the very existence of hypnosis. On the other hand, there were the moral objections to hypnosis put forward by the Swiss school (Dubois of Berne). These disputes, which were exceedingly bitter, as is often the case with controversies in psychology, and in which other than psychological arguments were used, broke Bernheim down and finally reduced him to an ever-increasing insistence that there was no such thing as hypnosis. But if he gave up hypnosis, he retained suggestion, and this position brought him the animosity of his former followers (a third front) who protested against this complete assimilation of hypnosis to suggestion. Bernheim felt that his view "deprived the hypnotists of all their prestige". "They disowned me and excluded me from their number" (op. cit., p. xii), he added bitterly.

In addition to Bernheim, Janet also had some influence on certain workers interested in the theory of hypnosis. These workers started from the idea of "dissociation", according to which, briefly, certain streams of consciousness may become split off and assume a quality of "automatism". This process may reach a point at which there are several parallel personalities, as in cases of spontaneous somnambulism or of "multiple personality" (the literature provides a host of examples, the most famous being the cases of Mary Reynolds in 1811, and Azam's Felida and Flournoy's Helen Smith* at the end of the nineteenth century (44, French version). This mechanism was said to explain induced somnambulism and other hypnotic phenomena such as partial dissociation.

Some American authors, contemporaries of Janet, took his work as a basis, for example, McDougall (142), Morton Prince (175) and Boris Sidis (205). An interesting summary of this work can be found in the book by Brenman and Gill (34).

The unconscious plays an important part in the mechanism of psychological "dissociation". But, although he anticipated the importance of the unconscious, Janet did not interpret it in a dynamic sense and did not emphasize the motivational processes. This step was taken by Freud, and we shall see in a later chapter the influence which his ideas have had on the theory of hypnosis.

---

*The last of these cases is particularly dramatic, and surpasses in this respect even the story of Bridy Murphy, which made headlines in America in 1955.

Psychoanalytic Theories

ORIGINALLY, psychoanalytic theories of hypnosis were directed mainly to the problem of the gratification of the instinctual needs of the subject. In this context, the hypnotic situation consisted of a certain mode of transference.

The term "transference", although one of the most commonly used terms in the psychoanalytic vocabulary, is not easy to define. Appreciable differences could be pointed to between the various definitions given. We may, however, as a sort of common denominator, regard transference as the carrying over to the person of the therapist of emotions experienced in the past by the patient in relation to certain significant figures – parents or parent substitutes such as nurses, teachers and the like. We may similarly regard counter-transference as a comparable phenomenon involving the carrying over of the therapist's emotions to the person of the patient.

For Ferenczi (1909, 76), Freud's disciple, hypnosis involved a reactivation of the Oedipus complex, with its accompanying love and fear. It followed that there were two types of hypnosis, a "maternal" type based on love and a "paternal" type based on fear.

Freud develops his views on hypnosis in his *Group Psychology and the Analysis of the Ego* (1921). He insists upon the erotic aspect of the hypnotic relationship. "The hypnotic relation", he says, "is the devotion of someone in love to an unlimited degree but with sexual satisfaction excluded" (82, p. 77). But hypnosis "itself exhibits some features which are not met by the rational explanation we have hitherto given of it as a state of being in love, with the directly sexual tendencies excluded. There is still a great deal in it which we must recognize as unexplained and mystical" (op. cit., p. 79). Freud also insists upon the submissive aspect of the hypnotic relationship. The hypnotist takes the place of the subject's ego ideal and plays the role of the omnipotent father of the primitive horde.

Schilder (196) likewise insists upon the libidinal ties between hypnotist and hypnotized* and upon the identification of subject

---

*On the basis of their experiments. Gill and Brenman (87) consider that the erotic fantasies which have free play during the induction of hypnosis are no more frequent than in any other psychotherapeutic relationship.

with practitioner. In endowing the physician with the omnipotence of magic, the patient is expressing his own infantile fantasies. Schilder was also the first psychoanalyst to draw attention to physiological and somatic factors and to show the importance of their integration with the psychological factors. He thus opened up a profitable field of research which was to lead to a revision of the theory of hypnosis.

Jones (108) approaches the problem from the point of view of narcissism and the constituent elements of the ego ideal. Narcissism is for him the essential agent of auto- and hetero-suggestion; hypnosis involves regression to an auto-erotic stage. Fenichel (75) specifies the subject's libidinal fixations and insists upon the satisfaction of pre-genital (oral) impulses of a passive receptive type.

During the last few years, hypnosis has benefited from new developments in psychoanalytic theory, especially theories of ego-psychology. Brenman, Gill and Knight (1952, 33) have emphasized the importance of ego-psychology for the understanding of hypnosis. They made an experimental study of "fluctuations in depth of hypnosis and their implications for ego-functioning". Their work has emphasized the complexity of the trance phenomenon, which is of such a nature as to defy any attempt to understand it purely in quantitative terms, according to its degree of depth. We have, in any case, no technique for measuring the depth of a trance. The subject's assertions about his subjective experience still provide the best criterion, provided, of course, that we have an intelligent subject capable of analysing his experience. Brenman, Gill and Knight conducted their study on the basis of their subjects' reports. After obtaining records of sequences of hypnotic sessions in which a variation in the trance had been indicated by the subject, they presented these records to judges who knew the past histories of these patients, by way of validation. The judges had to "predict" from the context of the session whether the subject would indicate any variation and in which direction it would be. The authors found that the deepening or lightening of the trance might represent a defence mechanism. The depth of the trance changed when the impulse-defence balance was threatened. Thus a change in the trance might follow the appearance of hostility in the transference relationship. The subject goes into a deeper trance state not so much to obtain infantile libidinal gratification as to deny his aggression by exaggerating his submissiveness. The deepening of the trance, like the lightening, may sometimes serve to yield libidinal gratification and sometimes serve as a defence.

One of our own cases was an old man in poor general health (blood urea nitrogen varying from 85 to 130 mg. per 100 c.c.) who had suffered from persistent insomnia since reaching adulthood. Massive doses of hypnotics which actually endangered his health gave him only short periods of sleep. This subject, a man of strong personality, of the "manager" type, had, in spite of his serious azotemia, retained a vigour and presence which astonished his doctors, whom he treated with aggressive scepticism. A hypnotic state was induced at the first session, but very quickly he fell asleep, snoring. This insomniac, who had been taking massive doses of drugs to get sleep, fell asleep immediately at a single signal. He slept as long as we were beside him. Post-hypnotic suggestion, however, had only a temporary effect. This development may have been the result of instinctual mechanisms "allowing" sleep as long as the vigilant therapist was present. But it is just as likely to have been a form of defence aimed at interrupting a certain kind of communication with the therapist.

Again, we often, in the course of our researches with Muriel Cahen (45), came across subjects who gave a faithful account of their experiences, and observed that the fluctuations in the trance were related to the progress of the therapeutic relationship and the material handled.

By introducing the concept of transference, psychoanalytic theories clarified the hypnotic relationship, but did not succeed in giving a proper explanation of it, for transference is involved in any psychotherapeutic relationship and cannot account for the specific characteristics of the hypnotic relationship.

Ida Macalpine (141) has shown that hypnotizing involves the immediate development of a transference relationship analogous to that which is established more gradually during the course of a psychoanalysis. According to her, in both cases the means by which the transference is achieved are essentially the same; the subject is placed in an infantile situation to which he adapts by regression. It might be added that in the hypnotic relationship, the transference is generally activated by gratification; the hypnotist bestows his words, and according to Fisher (78), suggestions are received like food. He writes, "Suggestions are accepted or rejected in relation to the degree of anxiety or gratification activated by certain incorporative or expulsive fantasies, e.g., the suggestion is accepted when it is equated unconsciously with the oral incorporation of a 'good' substance, and rejected when it takes on the meaning of a 'bad' substance" (p. 435). From this point of view, if the subject is hypnotized by verbal suggestion, he may be regarded as having incorporated a "good" substance. Fisher adds that "the same impulse dynamics are involved in the suggestive process in analytic patients and in normal subjects in nontherapeutic relationships" (ibid.).

In psychoanalytic relationships, different in this respect from hypnotic, the therapist to start with does not give much, since he remains silent; it is an atmosphere of frustration in which the transference develops. Some differences, of course, are not always so pronounced, and the subject's experience may take intermediate forms.

Recently (1962), Nacht (160) has questioned "the rule of neutrality when strictly applied and of its corollary the rule of frustration". Transference, under these conditions, could only "originate and develop" with difficulty. It is the innermost, unconscious attitude of the analyst, an attitude made up of benevolence, attentive receptiveness and flexibility, which gets the patient "involved" in the treatment. Even though the analyst is silent, the patient "should sense a watchful presence which *really exists** and is felt as helpful". Nacht goes even further, in that he thinks that the non-verbal communication is the more important and that "the spoken word is, at least at the beginning of treatment, an element which confirms and increases the separation between them [patient and analyst] and separation... engenders fear". Meares (220) holds that in hypnosis, verbal communication to a certain extent hinders regression and he describes a technique of non-verbal induction in which hypnosis is induced by the setting (cf. 113). We thus see how the roles of speech and of silence in the therapeutic relationship are differently estimated by different authors. These factors will certainly have a different effect according to the stage reached in the development of the therapeutic situation.

A decisive step towards understanding the connexion between transference and hypnosis was taken when, in 1944, an article appeared by Kubie and Margolin entitled, *The process of hypnotism and the nature of the hypnotic state* (126). After the fruitful insights of Schilder, this article might be said to represent the first real attempt deriving from psychoanalysis to formulate a theory of hypnosis which takes account of both physiological and psychological factors. The authors make a very important distinction, with regard to hypnosis, which they themselves define as follows. "Science has gradually come to accept the fact of hypnotism; but adequate explanations of it are wanting still. In part this is due to failure to recognize that there are two quite different aspects of the phenomenon to describe and understand: namely, the hypnotic process and the hypnotic state. These differ on both psychological and physiological levels" (126, p. 611).

This distinction is especially important in relation to transference. Kubie and Margolin found that transference was not an indispensable condition for the induction of hypnosis, which can be achieved by purely physical manipulations.† It therefore appears that transference, when it appears at the induction stage, is not necessarily the cause of the subsequent hypnotic state.‡

---

*Author's italics.

† In a paper as early as 1942, Kubie and Margolin (125) describe a physiological method of induction in which the subject concentrated upon his own respiration, which is used as a hypnogenic stimulus.

‡ Whether transference itself can play the part of an inducing agent has not yet been made clear. It may indeed be asked if transference can ever be isolated. For example, are the hypnoidal states which occur spontaneously during a

On the contrary, it appears that sensory-motor manipulation is sufficient to produce the hypnotic state with all the psychological changes on the part of the subject which this involves. Kubie and Margolin, on the basis of this discovery,* have attempted a synthesis between psychoanalytic and Pavlovian theories. They think that in the induction phase there is progressive elimination of stimuli, except for those coming from the hypnotist. This could be explained by a central zone of cortical excitation surrounded by a zone of inhibition. The authors interpret this psychologically as a de-differentiation of the Ego and the external world, represented by the hypnotist; the subject ends by failing to distinguish between himself and the outside world. He thus regresses to an infantile state, with the hypnotist playing the role previously played by the parents.

The book by the psychoanalysts Gill and Brenman (87)† which appeared in 1959 represents an extremely valuable contribution to hypnology. The authors here attempt to integrate certain data from experimental psychology and even from physiology with the new psychoanalytic ideas (ego-psychology) which they had previously used. They point out that up to the time at which they were writing, psychoanalytic explanations of hypnosis had revolved about masochism (the relationship of subject to hypnotist being a masochistic type of relationship) and transference (reactivation of the Oedipus complex). In other

---

psychoanalytic session due entirely to the interpersonal relationship experienced by the subject, or are they partly due to physical factors such as silence, lying stretched out, immobility and the like, which play the same part as sensory-motor manipulation and represent a particular case of "afferent isolation"? One does, of course, sometimes come across subjects who go into a hypnotic state at the very first contact with the practitioner, before the factors we have been talking about can possibly have had any effect. It is tempting to regard these cases as showing the influence of transference alone.

*The idea of perhaps being able to produce regressive psychological phenomena by sensory-motor manipulation ("sensory deprivation" before this was actually used) occurs in the study by Kubie and Margolin (126, 1944). The work of the Hebb school has provided experimental confirmation of this idea, although the Montreal workers did not start from Kubie and Margolin's hypothesis. It was the search for an explanation of the mechanism of brain-washing which led to the discoveries about "sensory deprivation".

†Gill and Brenman are at present training analysts, the former at the Psychoanalytic Institute in San Francisco, the latter at the Austen Riggs Centre at Stockbridge. Their book is the fruit of many years' research conducted with lavish means (grants from several scientific foundations, and the use of several thousand psychology students, a hundred residents in psychiatry and a large number of patients as experimental subjects).

words, only instinctual forces had been involved. The "sensory-motor", somatic side of hypnosis had not been considered (except by Schilder and Kauders (197), and Kubie and Margolin (126)). It had remained in the field of experimental psychology.

The gulf which separates the experimentalists from the psychoanalysts seems to be lessening. The experimentalists are beginning to take unconscious motives into account and the analysts to turn their attention towards the part played by sensory-motor phenomena. Gill and Brenman start from the work of Kubie and Margolin, in which they see the first systematic attempt to integrate psychological and physiological phenomena. Basing their approach on Hartmann's ideas on the functional systems of the Ego (ego apparatuses) and their primary autonomy (93), they were able to investigate the sensory-motor problem in hypnosis. Finally, the work of Kris on regression in the service of the Ego enabled them to regard hypnosis as a regression of the same kind. At the same time, Gill and Brenman have been greatly influenced by the work of Hebb and his school at Montreal on "sensory deprivation". This has also been referred to as "sensory isolation" and "partial afferent isolation" (Kubie). It involves depriving the individual of all sensory input, for example by shutting him up in a cubical box (Bexton et al., 22) or immersing him in a tank of water with a mask to breathe through (Lilly, 139). After some time, regressive phenomena appear, sometimes accompanied by marked mental disturbance (hallucinations, depression, reverie and the like).* The number of publications on sensory deprivation has increased over the past few years (208).

For Gill and Brenman (87), hypnosis involves two "regression-producing" factors, the relational and motivational factors (transference) and physical manipulation (sensory deprivation). The latter consists, as Kubie and Margolin had already shown,

---

*In a paper given in 1960, Kubie (124) foresaw that a man sent into space would be submitted to such "sensory deprivation" (weightlessness, immobility, complete silence and absence of all communication) that he would fall into a hypnoidal state of reverie or waking dream. It has been shown that the cosmonauts who remained in space for several days did not react in this manner. Their isolation was not so complete as Kubie had imagined, since they maintained communication with the Earth and with one another. No doubt also training and motivation had something to do with the way in which they reacted. It may, nevertheless, be remarked that these factors did not prevent the space- woman, Valentina Terechkova, from unexpectedly having a nap during her flight.

in the limitation of the contact of the subject with the outside world entirely to the stimulation provided by the hypnotist. Thus there is a double process in hypnosis. The hypnotist induces the regression by two mechanisms — by his effect upon infantile impulses and by the reduction of the sensory-motor and ideational field. Hypnosis is thus for Gill and Brenman "*a particular kind of regressive process which may be initiated either by sensori-motor ideational deprivation or by the stimulation of an archaic relationship to the hypnotist*"* (87, pp. xix–xx), and they add that "when the regressive process has been set into motion by *either one** of these two kinds of factors, phenomena characteristic of the other kind begin to emerge" (*ibid.*). In practice, the hypnotist uses both *simultaneously.* The authors define the hypnotic state proper as "an induced psychological regression, issuing, in the setting of a particular regressed relationship between two people, in a relatively stable state which includes a subsystem of the ego with various degrees of control of the ego apparatuses" (op. cit., p. xxiii).

Thus the ego is not eliminated in the hypnotized subject, as was formerly believed. What we have is the ego modified by a particular regressive process. Gill and Brenman advance a hypothesis to the effect that "*every psychotherapeutic situation is to some extent an invitation to the patient to regress; that such regression usually takes place in greater or lesser amounts in all psychotherapies where the patient is reached at all; and that when hypnosis is used in psychotherapy we can observe this phenomenon more closely because it is greatly intensified*"* (op. cit., p. 328). The authors add, "We would go so far as to venture the speculation that it is precisely in this regression, and the way it is dealt with by the therapist — with or without the use of hypnosis — that the secret lies of maintaining an optimal affective involvement for the patient in the therapeutic process" (*ibid.*). They also think, on the basis of their own clinical explorations, that "in some contexts, what we have called the 'regressive trends' inherent in hypnosis are psychotherapeutically serviceable; in others they are useless if not dangerous" (p. 331).

It should be noted that, although Gill and Brenman based their approach on the work of Kubie and Margolin, their conclusions

---

* Author's italics.

have on some points been challenged by Kubie (124). First of all, let us remember that Kubie and Margolin (125) insisted on the possibility of inducing hypnosis without anyone in the role of hypnotist. They thus raised the question of whether hypnosis, by its very nature, implies an interpersonal relationship. To this controversial question Kubie provides a subtle and brilliant answer which, however, is only a working hypothesis. Paradoxically, Kubie, in this answer, considers hypnosis without a hypnotist as being *more* interpersonal than hypnosis with a hypnotist. Of the former, he writes, "Yet there is a presence in another sense; a hovering if unseen and unacknowledged presence, sometimes consciously perceived but more often preconsciously and/or unconsciously. This presence may represent the earliest protective figures of infancy, or much later figures of authority and protection. Therefore the past makes its inevitable contribution to the process of induction. Actually this is transference in purest culture, even when there is no present object, whether real or imagined, whether conscious or subliminal, to whom to assign the protective functions which in childhood we slowly learned to exercise for ourselves. This is probably the origin and essence of the ancient fantasy of a guardian angel, someone to guard me when I am helpless in sleep" (124). (In the case of hypnosis without a hypnotist we would suggest the use of the term "autogenous", "endogenous" or "anonymous" transference in contrast to "heterogeneous", "exogenous" or "personalized" transference.)

The author adds that the inability to manage these protective functions is at the root of human psychopathology; so that "the study of the phenomenology of hypnotism has broad and inclusive significance for the understanding of human nature in health and illness" (*ibid.*).*

Gill and Brenman, contrary to the views of Kubie and Margolin, consider that hypnosis proper can only occur when there is a direct relationship established between subject and hypnotist. "It is a major thesis of this book," they write, "that the relationship

---

*This anticipation recalls Pavlov's ideas on hypnosis as a means to the understanding of schizophrenia. Recently, an American author, King (115), has held schizophrenia to be a suggestive phenomenon analogous to hypnosis; while Margaretta Bowers (29) also regards schizophrenia as a sort of malignant and permanent autohypnosis.

with the hypnotist *is** of the essence of hypnosis, and that when procedures are carried out which are in significant ways similar to the induction manipulations which we have described — but do not involve human contact (for example, the experiments of Bexton *et al.*) — the resulting phenomena bear important similarities to hypnosis, but are yet different from it" (87, p. 143). Thus transference "in purest culture" (autogenous transference), which according to Kubie should occur where there is no hypnotist present, would not occur with a genuine hypnotic state. A "heterogeneous" transference is, according to Gill and Brenman, an indispensable condition of hypnosis.

The difference between the ideas of Gill and Brenman on the one hand and those of Kubie on the other can be reduced to a question of definition. It might be put in this way. All three authors admit a beginning of induction by manipulation of the sensory-motor, physical level. But for the state to be called hypnosis, Gill and Brenman also require that there should be transference. Kubie, on the other hand, extends the term "hypnosis" to include states without transference (introducing, however, the special sense of transference "in purest culture"). He insists that induction can be obtained without the actual presence of any other human being. Gill and Brenman refuse to employ the term "hypnosis" for this case, and speak of related states. For them, "hypnosis" always involves an *inter*-personal process. For Kubie, it can refer to a uniquely *intra*-personal experience. The essential point for Kubie is that, in hypnosis, the subject "abdicates the use of his own native, self-protecting and alerting mechanisms, placing himself and his sense of 'security' in the hands of another", whether that other be real or imaginary.

According to Gill and Brenman, again, transference develops automatically when the hypnotist is present. For Kubie, this is not necessarily the case. The hypnotist may represent only a physical, sensory-motor field, without his presence giving rise to a "hetero-transferential" relationship. Kubie likewise thinks that it is by no means established that an archaic relationship inevitably accompanies the process of regression, whether at the induction stage or during the hypnotic state itself, or whatever the form of hypnosis, with or without a hypnotist.

---

*Author's italics.

As far as the regression itself is concerned, Kubie sees it as an accompaniment of hypnosis, but doubts whether it has any explanatory value. It is a "metaphor to describe the outcome of several processes" (124, p. 49). Kubie insists strongly on the danger of explaining a phenomenon by one of its consequences. For him, transference, counter-transference and the different regressive and progressive currents are epiphenomena. But what, above all, we must try to find out is by what "trigger mechanism" the way is opened into (or out of) the hypnotic state. Kubie attaches much importance to these "transitional" processes,* because our understanding of all human psychology, both normal and pathological, seems to him to depend largely on knowledge of the processes by which we pass from one state of psychological organization to another. Hypnosis seems to him in this respect a privileged field of research, since the processes in question are so readily controlled in it. We must therefore, he says, discover how they are activated and their joint determination by physiological and psychological factors should be investigated by psychologists, psychoanalysts, neurophysiologists, neurobiochemists, pharmacologists and so on, in co-operation.

The most recent contribution (1963) to the psychoanalytic theory of hypnosis is that of Harold Stewart (210). He likewise modifies the views of Freud and Ferenczi, according to which the hypnotic relationship is mainly a masochistic and libidinal surrender of the hypnotized subject to the hypnotist. Stewart develops the ideas of Gill and Brenman that the hypnotic relationship involves not only gratification of instinctual needs but also a complex balance between impulses and defences, in which hostility plays an important part. In other words, Stewart takes up the notion that the hypnotic subject has an ambivalent attitude toward the hypnotist, loving and at the same time hating him, the latter aspect actually being the more important. Stewart reports that he had observed that interpretation of libidinal impulses to the subject did not affect the depth of hypnosis, while drawing the subject's attention to his feelings of hostility had the effect of lightening or even abolishing the trance. This means that if the

---

* A Soviet author (207), using the work of Wedenski on parabiosis, has recently (1962) emphasized the importance of the idea of the lability of physiological processes for understanding hypnosis (he has even attempted to quantify this lability, relating it to the "chronaxia" measurable by Bourguignon's apparatus).

patient is hypnotized, his hostile feelings are somehow integrated in such a way as to be tolerable to him. Stewart speculates as to how this may come about. He postulates that when the hypnotized subject feels and says that he is in the control of the hypnotist, it is only at the conscious level. In fact, for the unconscious, the opposite is the case; the subject is in control of the situation. The author's reasoning is as follows:

"The hypnotic state is based on a deception — that the hypnotist must pretend to the patient that he is omnipotent, if he is to induce a hypnotic trance." But the *unconscious*, which is "aware" of this pretence, overcomes it by a feeling of "omnipotently forcing the hypnotist to this deception, and is thereby in control of the hypnotic situation". Thus, "far from the trance relationship being only a passive masochistic identification and surrender on the part of the subject, the unconscious dynamic content is also an aggressive attack on the hypnotist . . . The hypnotic trance can be conceived of as a collusion between hypnotist and subject to deny his aggressive controlling attack on the hypnotist, and at the same time is an expression of this attack."

On the basis of these theoretical speculations, Stewart advances new hypotheses to explain hypnotic phenomena. According to him, two situations may arise. "The first is of a heightened performance in the use of the subject's ability for reality testing, since anxieties about the hypnotist as a rival in this sphere can be dispensed with. The second situation is the opposite of this, i.e., the denial of the ability for reality testing, as, for example, in positive and negative hallucinations, analgesias, aphonia, etc., and this can be conceived of as an inner attack on the self which is under the sway of the reality-principle, and would result from fears of retaliation from the attacked hypnotist or of the unconscious guilt felt for the attack."

Stewart also gives an explanation of the ability to recall and abreact hidden memories. He writes, "Freud suggested (1921) that the hypnotist is put in place of the subject's ego ideal (superego), but I would suggest that the superego is put in place of the hypnotist, and this projected superego is controlled by the subject, with the collusion of the hypnotist. Thus the subject now feels free from the power of the superego to a large extent, and can give fairly free rein to the emergence of previously repressed memories."

Hypnosis and Sleep

THE Abbé Faria (72) was the first to refer to the hypnotic state as "lucid sleep". Since then, the terms "hypnotic sleep", "induced sleep", "artificial sleep" and so on have been used. Writers like Schilder and Kauders, Kretschmer, Stokvis and others have upheld this relation from the physiological point of view by locating the physiological basis of hypnosis in the sub-cortical sleep-regulating centres. For the Pavlovian school, a state of partial cortical inhibition is involved. With the discovery of the fundamental role of the reticular formation of the brain-stem in wakefulness, there has also emerged a theory attributing particular significance to this formation in the mechanism of hypnosis (216). American authors are opposed to the sleep theory. They consider that respiration, pulse and all the other physiological concomitants of hypnosis are no different from what they are in the waking state. The patellar reflex, in particular, is never abolished.

After the coming of the EEG, the controversy was carried on with renewed vigour. The Russians claim to have demonstrated the similarity of hypnosis and sleep as indicated by the EEG. Their conclusions do not appear justified. They distinguish electrically between the three stages of hypnosis, although clinically the existence of these stages does not rest upon objective criteria. The Americans, on the other hand, have failed to find any evidence from the EEG of similarity between hypnosis and sleep. Other workers, such as Israel and Rohmer (101), speak of "pre-sleep". The present writer and Kramarz (46)* took EEG records of subjects under hypnosis. In the majority of the subjects, the record was unaltered by hypnosis, but in certain subjects, the interpretation of the record was somewhat equivocal. We found some EEGs which did suggest modifications in the state of consciousness, with decreasing or increasing wakefulness; slowing down of the EEG, indicating a state of pre-sleep,

---

*This paper also contains a critical review of the literature on the subject.

40

and desynchronization of the alpha rhythm and accentuation of ocular artefacts suggesting a state of hypervigilance.

Apart from similarities of a physiological nature there is also a tendency on the psychological level, especially among the psychoanalysts, to see common features between hypnosis and sleep. Brenman (32) thinks that, up to a certain point, hypnosis and sleep are comparable psychologically. Bellak (19) regards hypnosis as a "special case of the self-excluding function of the Ego", which is also found in sleep. What happens in hypnosis is the same as what happens in the automatic performance of some task, i.e., topological regression to a pre-conscious level of functioning. In the automatic performance of a task, a fragment of the cognitive function still persists; in hypnosis, this function is controlled by the hypnotist. For Bellak, there is no fundamental difference, in terms of psychodynamics, between hypnosis and sleep, other than quantitative differences in the degree of exclusion of the Ego.

Kubie, with his usual circumspection, warns us against attempts to explain hypnosis by sleep. In doing so, he says, we are proceeding "as though we understood sleep and as though the precise relationship between the hypnotic state, sleep and dream had been clearly defined when in fact neither assumption is valid" (124, p. 48). For Kubie, on the other hand, it is hypnosis which, when we understand it properly, will throw light on the mechanism of sleep.

Animal Hypnosis

EXPERIMENTS in animal hypnosis actually preceded those in human hypnosis, in point of time. In 1646, in Rome, the Jesuit Father Athanasius Kircher conducted his "Experimentum mirabile de imaginatione gallinae". This famous experiment really provided the basis for the various techniques which were to be used later, and its interpretation raises the essential theoretical problems still being discussed today. It therefore merits an account in general terms.

A hen with its feet tied was set on a board, lying either on its belly or on its side. After a period of excitement, it calmed down again and a line was then drawn in chalk on the board, starting from its beak. If its feet were now freed, it would remain still. To "awaken" it, it was necessary to strike it a light blow or make a noise. According to Kircher, the hen calmed down from the moment when, in the face of its futile efforts to escape, it "submitted to its conqueror". When its "conqueror" liberated it, it still remained in the same place, because its "vehemens animalis imaginatio" interpreted the line as a bond and it remained stupefied. Thus Father Kircher, by invoking "fear", "submission" and the hen's "imagination" gave a kind of psychological orientation to his explanation. This psychological orientation was to be adopted by many workers and to show itself equally profitable in the interpretation of human hypnosis.

Among the numerous experimenters who were interested in animal hypnosis, especially from the end of the nineteenth century, we may mention Czermak, Preyer, Danilewski, Mangold, Volgyesi and Svorad. The experiments of these and other writers covered the most divergent species—mammals, birds, reptiles, batrachians, insects, spiders, crustaceans, fish and so on. The phenomena reported were given various names, sometimes corresponding to real differences in the phenomena, but often simply betraying the ideological, physiological or psychological orientations of the authors. As far as actual technique is

42

concerned, Kircher's experiment has often been repeated, sometimes in a much simplified form. In the last resort, the technique
consists simply in immobilizing the hen in an unfamiliar position.
Many other procedures have been used, but all amount to putting
the animal in an unfamiliar position or situation, for example, suddenly turning it on its back (the usual procedure), staring fixedly
at it, hooding it or (with birds) swinging it repeatedly up and
down, and so on. The hypnotizability of animals is very variable. Hens are particularly amenable, while cats and dogs are
considered particularly resistant.

Fig. 1. – Experimentum mirabile. (After Kircher.)

In the animal world, there are cases of spontaneous hypnosis,
occurring without any experimentation. Some invertebrates
spontaneously go into a sort of cataleptic state, like the spider
which a bright light "freezes" in its web. Again, some animals can
exert on others an influence which reduces them to a hypnotic
state. In a species of large spider, the *Galeodes caspicus turkes-
tanus,* described by Heymons, the female tries to devour the
male while he is courting her. In order to be able to copulate, the
male "hypnotizes" the female by planting his claws in her
abdomen.* When copulation is completed, the female attacks her

*Schilder (196) takes this example as supporting the hypothesis of a libidinal
component in human hypnosis.

partner, who is in general weaker but speedier than she is. Thus he often succeeds in escaping with his life. Finally, it is well known that snakes "fascinate" rats, birds and the like, and that this may sometimes be mutual.

From a theoretical point of view, animal hypnosis first of all raises the question of its biological significance. Opinions on this point are divided. For Pavlov (168), animal hypnosis is a self-preservative reflex; if the animal does not find safety in fighting or in flight, it adopts a motionless position so as not to provoke by movement the aggressive behaviour of the attacker. Freud expresses himself in similar terms. Hypnosis "contains an additional element of paralysis derived from the relation between someone with superior power and someone who is without power and helpless — which may afford a transition to the hypnosis of terror which occurs in animals" (82, p. 79). But other writers (Mangold, Rabaud, Svorad) remark that the immobilization reflex has no utility for certain animals, while some to which it would be of value do not have it (e.g., *Scarites lavigatus*). The same reflex is even harmful to certain arthropods (e.g., *Nehria psammodes* and *Brachynus crepitans*).

Another problem is raised by the nature of the hypnosis. In their explanations, writers have given special emphasis to some particular aspect of the phenomena, some insisting upon the emotional aspect (fear, submission and so on), others on the neurophysiological aspect (tonic reflex, cortical inhibition and the like). But none of these explanations is adequate, because they are one-sided and distinguish too rigidly between mental and physical factors. A point of view which at least makes an attempt at synthesis was introduced by Schilder and Kauders (197). Although they attribute considerable importance to physiological factors, they emphasize that these are not the only factors which must be taken into consideration. According to them, we cannot, for example, yet say for certain whether motor inhibition in animals is entirely the result of motor changes, or whether it is bound up with mental changes. This double aspect is equally relevant when we are concerned with human hypnosis. Schilder and Kauders consider that, in general, despite variations due to differences in cerebral organization, animal hypnosis and human hypnosis are fundamentally identical.

Schilder has provided a new outlook on the explanation of

human hypnosis, an outlook which combines attention to the motivational aspect with a consideration of the organic substratum. One of his collaborators, H. Hartmann (93), has effected a change of viewpoint in psychoanalysis, by an increased emphasis on the ego and consequently the body in relation to instinctual forces. This change has had repercussions on the theory of hypnosis, as is evidenced, in particular, by the work of Gill and Brenman (87). As we have already indicated, Gill and Brenman have achieved a synthesis (cf. p. 34) between the ideas of psychoanalytic ego-psychology and some recent theories of experimental psychology. For them, hypnosis is a process of regression which can be induced either physically (by sensory-motor deprivation) or psychologically.

In their book (87), Gill and Brenman make only one reference to animal hypnosis, in connexion with the ideas of Kubie and Margolin on the importance of disturbance of motor activity in living creatures. Kubie and Margolin take up Pavlov's idea that any disturbance of motor activity in an animal constitutes a first step towards the induction of hypnotic immobilization. For them, the human subject who is required to gaze fixedly at some point is in the same kind of position as the animal which is prevented from moving its head. This line of thought, as Gill and Brenman emphasize, for the first time establishes a link between animal hypnosis and human hypnotic states, "via the interference with an apparatus of the organism vital in maintaining its contact with the stimuli of the outer world" (87, p. 128).

Gill and Brenman, however, do not themselves suggest any explanation of animal hypnosis based on their conception of human hypnosis. It seems to us that their ideas provide an interesting starting-point, and we should like, by using this starting-point, ourselves to suggest a new theoretical formulation of animal hypnosis. What seems to us the essential element in animal hypnosis is the situational factor, i.e., the change which occurs in the physical and emotional relations of the animal to its environment. As a result of the various manipulations to which it has been subjected, the animal is in a kind of state of "sensory deprivation", to which it reacts by adopting an attitude of torpor and immobility which may be interpreted as regressive.

It should be noted that immobilization is not always sufficient to effect hypnotic immobility. It is sometimes also necessary to put the animal in an uncomfortable or unfamiliar position. This changes the animal's mode of maintaining contact with the world and constitutes "psychological stress". The experiments of Bonfils and Lambling (26) on rats are instructive. Rats prevented from making any movement whatever, after several hours in a state of great agitation, develop an ulcer. Guinea-pigs similarly treated (Brodie and Hanson, 36; Levy *et al.*, 133) also become agitated and finally contract the same disorder, though less frequently. By turning guinea-pigs on their backs, however, one can easily provoke a state of hypnotic immobility. The guinea-pig or rat immobilized by restraint maintains contact with the environment. It is under continuous stress and consequently ends by developing an ulcer. When the guinea-pig is turned on its back, hypnotized, contact with the outside world is lost and the animal reacts to this unfamiliar situation by becoming "un-conscious", a kind of global regression which seems to be bene-ficial to the organism in the long run.

The guinea-pig, however, remains in this position only for a short time, and we cannot say that its condition would remain the same if it were to be kept in the same position for as long a time as was necessary for an ulcer to be produced by the restraint technique used in the experiments mentioned above. Liberson's work (134) is of interest here. He succeeded in producing prolonged hypnotic states in guinea-pigs. He subjected them to a series of immobilizations ending abruptly with a sensory stimulus. The duration of the immobilization increased as the experiment went on. At a certain point, which Liberson called the "break-ing-point", the animals, while appearing as if "stuck" to the board on which they were lying, showed exophthalmus, with over-extended extremities at times ani-mated by a fine tremor. They lost weight and finally died.

The question is whether this can be attributed to hypnotic immobilization. It must be pointed out that the immobilization is not accompanied by tension until the "breaking-point" is reached, so that the tension appears more likely to be the result of psychological frustration consequent upon the unsuccessful attempts of the animals to get up. Again, the prolonged immobilization achieved through this frustration mechanism is not necessarily comparable to hypnotic immo-bilization proper, which is characterized by "relaxation" and may be interpreted as a posture assumed "spontaneously" by the animals as a kind of defence. The immobilization with tension to which the animals were subjected in Liberson's experiments, on the other hand, appears to be the result of a long series of re-straints. Here, of course, one can only speculate, in the absence of experimental work to justify more definite views.

We now propose the following definition. Animal hypnosis constitutes regressive behaviour characterized by immobility and torpor. This regressive behaviour may be induced by various procedures which put the animal in an unfamiliar situation or position and which all have the effect of changing the normal pattern of the animal's sensory-motor and emotional interaction with its environment. As one ascends in the animal kingdom, the increasing development of mental functions means that emotional factors (which no doubt already operate to some degree in the inferior animals) play an increasingly important part in the induction of hypnosis. Even so, sensory deprivation as such is still important in man. Thus, a living organism always requires to interact with the outside world, and if this interaction is interrupted or altered, the organism may react by adopting a regressive attitude. This is precisely what happens in both animal and human hypnosis, and this common factor provides the basis for the fundamental similarity of the two forms of hypnosis.*

The reader will now understand why we have spent so long on the theoretical problems posed by animal hypnosis. Human hypnosis has not so far been satisfactorily explained, and this being so, the study of animal hypnosis may represent a valuable return to first principles. In general, the study of animal behaviour is useful in helping us to understand instinctual processes in man.† It is therefore regrettable that studies of animal hypnosis have been getting fewer for some years; for, appearing as it does in simpler forms more amenable to experiment, animal hypnosis will one day, perhaps, throw some light upon problems of human hypnosis.

---

*We have seen the importance attached by Kubie (cf. p. 37) to the suppression of the "self-protecting . . . mechanisms" in the experience of human hypnosis. He uses similar terms when he mentions animal hypnosis. Referring to the psychophysiology of hypnosis, he writes, "Ask a man to fix his eyes on a slowly swirling centrifugal spiral; or else hold the head and neck of a fowl still with the beak to a chalk line. Any such manoeuvres, which immobilize all of the critical alerting mechanisms, may give rise to similar phenomena" (hypnoidal states, 124).

†This is the point of view which guided M. Henri Ey (71) in the publication of the collective volume *Psychiatrie Animale*, to which zoologists, veterinary surgeons and psychiatrists contributed under his editorship. This volume contains a chapter by the present writer on animal hypnosis in which the points made here are more fully developed. The chapter also contains the bibliographical references for the authors cited here.

Hypnotizability

THE problem of hypnotizability is a fundamental one. A question inevitably asked by physicians and laymen alike is whether everyone can by hypnotized, and conversely, whether everyone can hypnotize. Let us start with the former question. Before embarking upon a consideration of the problem in detail, we may make one simple point. There are on the one hand subjects who can be hypnotized by anyone, excellent hypnotic subjects. (There were professional subjects in Liébeault's time, and the present writer came across some before the last War at the Vienna psychiatric clinic, where they collaborated as subjects for the instruction of students who wanted to take up hypnosis.) On the other hand, there are some subjects who will never be hypnotizable. Between these two extremes, there are subjects who are more or less hypnotizable, and who can be hypnotized by some practitioners and not by others.

This view is generally accepted, but Gill and Brenman (87) think that the hypnotizability of a subject is relatively constant. They conducted a series of experiments designed to increase the hypnotizability of difficult subjects by varying the methods used and the hypnotists, and found that these variations made very little difference.

Again, when we speak of hypnotizability, we must take account of the *degree* of hypnosis or depth of trance and the implications of relativity which this involves. Attempts have been made to express such things in percentages, with very variable results. The great difficulty is that we have no objective criteria by which to decide whether the subject is hypnotized, or how deeply. Bramwell (31) considered that all subjects were hypnotizable up to a certain point, and that deep trances could be obtained in from 10 to 20 per cent of cases. Bernheim had previously estimated that four-fifths of the hospital population were capable of going into a deep trance, while this proportion was only between one-fifth and one-sixth for his private patients.

48

The Factors Determining Hypnotizability

Hypnotizability depends upon two sets of factors, concerned respectively with the subject and the hypnotist. The personality of the subject has been studied from all points of view and no certain indications have emerged. No correlations have been found between hypnotizability and physical or psychological constitution, extraversion-introversion, race, sex, social status and so on. Projective techniques have been used but without conclusive results. No definite relation has been established between hypnotizability and particular illnesses.

Our own observations have indicated, however, that adolescents and adults suffering from enuresis are almost all hypnotizable, and this is also true, although to a lesser extent, of asthmatics. Kaufman (113) indicates that soldiers are generally highly amenable to hypnosis. During the Pacific campaign in the Second World War, he treated about 2,500 combatants, of whom the great majority were excellent subjects. This confirms the observations previously made by older authors like Liébeault and Bernheim, who referred in explanation to the passive obedience which soldiers are required to show. But Kubie (124), interpreting Kaufman's results, thinks that the doctor who gets the soldier out of the front line becomes for the soldier an omnipotent figure to whom he trusts for his protection.

A connexion has long been established between suggestibility and hypnotizability. For Bernheim, hypnosis was virtually reducible to suggestibility, though Janet took a different view of the matter, and wrote, "The phenomena of suggestion are independent of the hypnotic state; well-marked suggestibility may exist quite apart from artificial somnambulism, and suggestibility may be entirely lacking in one who is in a state of complete somnambulism. In a word, suggestibility does not vary simultaneously with somnambulism, and does not vary in the same direction" (105, p.282).

At the present time, Kubie (124) holds that suggestibility is not the cause but the consequence of the hypnotic state. In support of this view, he refers to the experiments in which he put a subject into a hypnotic state by means of an apparatus without any verbal suggestion (125). The patient thus hypnotized at once received the words of the hypnotist as if they had been his own. In other words, the "boundary" between hypnotist and hypnotized was, as it were, removed. Thus, hypnotizability depends upon "the ease with which an individual can internalize an external stimulus and make it part of himself" (op. cit., p. 49). The present writer and Muriel Cahen (45) conducted a study of the personality of the subject in a sample of forty patients, mostly "psychosomatic", and including both "good" and "bad" hypnotic subjects. Both interviews and tests were used in this study. No attempt was made to carry out a statistical analysis of the sample or of the results, since the study was made only on patients, without any control group. (In other countries, experiments have been conducted with "normal" populations, especially psychology students.) We simply collected some clinical data.

Among the refractory patients, we were able to distinguish two types—cases of voluntary refusal and cases not amenable to hypnosis. The majority had been chronic patients and had had surgical operations which had failed to remove their symptoms. All were socially maladjusted. All had very disturbed personalities and were examples of what may be called "somato-psychosis", of a very narcissistic nature. They gave the impression that their physical ills enabled them to maintain a relative psychological equilibrium. Contact with reality was precarious and control inadequate.

The "good" subjects were all well-adapted socially, with good contact with reality. If they suffered from conflicts, they had a fair margin of adjustment at their disposal. We found no cases among them of obsessional types. But in so far as the hysterical type extends into the normal, we may speak of a hysterical element in these subjects.

We have now come to the problem of *hysterics*. Much has been written on this problem. Hypnosis was long regarded as equivalent to hysteria. It was thought that hysterics were the only hypnotizable subjects. As a matter of fact, it is now thought that neurotics, in general, are less hypnotizable than normal people; and it may be said that certain severe hysterics are resistant to hypnosis. Since the hysterical symptom is bound up with emotions directed towards persons in the patient's past life, these patients reject new transference relationships with the hypnotist. It is as if they refused to reconsider the problem and to renounce their secondary gains. Less severe hysterics are good subjects. Hypnotizability can even be regarded as a prognostic indicator. When a hysterical subject can be hypnotized, he is still amenable to psychotherapy.

These clinical impressions are confirmed by the observations of Gill and Brenman (87). They verified experimentally that normal people are easier to hypnotize than neurotics, and that among the latter, hysterics are the best subjects, while not being as good subjects as normal people.

As far as perseverance in inducing a trance is concerned, some authors stop at three or four attempts, while others go beyond this. The German author, Vogt (225), was successful at the 300th session. In our view, success at the first session is very important, but it is not a requirement. For instance, we were successful in obtaining a trance with a hospitalized patient at the second attempt, three months after the first. Some subjects who are refractory to individual hypnosis may be hypnotized in a group, the group playing the role of protector against the patient's unconscious fears.

Turning now to the question of the hypnotist, we find two problems requiring attention—the technique used and the personality of the hypnotist. It is obvious that long experience and technical skill play a part. Technique must above all be supple and adaptable to different subjects. For good subjects, any technique will do; for difficult subjects, the technique must be more elaborate (see the second part of the present book). The first attempt is particularly important. This is perhaps why, at the Vienna psychiatric clinic, professional hypnotic subjects were employed. It is a good thing for the student to succeed at his first attempt.

There are no valid criteria for the *personality* of the hypnotist. This has been less studied than the personality of the subject. We have only some remarks by different authors. Back in the era of animal magnetism, authors were of the opinion that magnetizers should be free from anxiety and on guard against "imagination", since the subject would reflect the magnetiser's state of mind. But it certainly cannot be said that the ability to use hypnosis depends upon any particular personality structure. Just as there are different kinds of hypnosis (paternal and maternal), and just as the subject can be hypnotized for various reasons, so the motivation of the therapist may equally vary. According to Schilder, the hypnotist should be motivated by an unconscious desire for magical power and sexual domination of the patient.

The fear of these unconscious wishes may increase the resistance of some to the use of hypnosis. Breuer, for example, interrupted the treatment of Miss Anna O. for reasons of counter-transference and because of Mrs. Breuer's jealousy. Miss Anna O. was having a hysterical pregnancy and the imaginary confinement took place on the very day on which Breuer informed her that he was stopping the treatment. Jones (107) also informs us that the future Mrs. Freud identified with Mrs. Breuer and feared that she might herself one day be in the same situation. Her husband had to reassure her. The fact remains that Freud, although he had been interested by the treatment of Miss Anna O., of whom he had heard in November 1882, finally decided to use hypnosis only at the beginning of December 1887. He had occasionally used it since the summer of 1885, but from April 1886, when he began to have private patients, he had mostly used electrotherapy. From December 1887 until May 1889, he used hypnotic suggestion alone, and then also used the cathartic method. Jones (107) attributes this late use of the cathartic method to the more than reserved attitude of Charcot to Breuer's method, of which Freud had given him an account. It is possible that problems of counter-transference were also involved. The later incident is well known, of the patient who flung her arms round Freud's neck, and his reaction to this as given in his autobiography. "I was modest enough not to attribute the event to my own irresistible personal attraction, and I felt that I had now grasped the nature of the mysterious element that was at work behind hypnotism. In order to exclude it, or at all events to isolate it, it was necessary to abandon hypnotism" (81, p. 48). This was a fruitful act of desertion, since it was to lead Freud to the discovery of psychoanalysis . . .

According to Ferenczi (76), there are enormous differences in the rates of success for different hypnotists, these rates varying from 10 per cent to 80, 90 or even 96 per cent. Ferenczi draws attention to the impressive presence, social prestige and assurance of the therapist, and even such physical peculiarities as a black beard (which corresponded to the popular stereotype of the hypnotist at the time, whereas today the stage hypnotists tend rather to be clean-shaven and sporty in appearance). Finally, Ferenczi remarks that the very first time he practised hypnosis, his ignorance gave him a degree of self-confidence conducive to success, which he failed to retain later.

An American analyst who had done important work in hypnosis spoke to the present writer of the difficulties he experienced in hypnotizing after his personal analysis, and wondered whether his motives in hypnotizing had not been neurotic. His point was not valid, as the writer told him, since one might just as well regard as neurotic the inability to use what was considered an important research tool — which he readily admitted. We may, however, allow that the motives for hypnotizing may change after an analysis. Roughly, it might be said that what formerly served the interests of instinct-gratification is now of the nature of a sublimated activity. Perhaps also our practitioner, having become a psychoanalyst, was influenced by the opinion which has long prevailed among analysts that psychoanalysis, having succeeded hypnosis, does not need to have recourse to it. Thus his incapacity would not have resulted entirely from the solution by analysis of his deep-lying problems, but from motives arising from those socio-cultural factors the importance of which has been emphasized by Orne (164). A certain amount of non-conformity was necessary for psychoanalysts to begin to become interested in hypnosis. The increasing though still rather limited number of those interested is due to the fact that hypnosis appears as an exceptional instrument of research in the whole field of experimental psychopathology and psychotherapy, so that psychoanalysis, which is a child of hypnosis and has led to a better understanding of it, may in its turn be clarified by it.

A new attempt to clarify the problems of the personality of the hypnotist has been made by Gill and Brenman (87). They used the introspections of a number of hypnotists, collected observations from psychoanalysts who had treated hypnotists or who had used hypnosis themselves, and gave questionnaires to various research workers. They admit not having found any characteristic motivational pattern in the personality of the hypnotist. Their results do no more than suggest a few points. They found in the hypnotist a wish to play the role of omnipotent parental figure in relation to the subject, a wish which, after all, can be found at the root of any medical vocation, and especially psychiatry. Another quality common in hypnotists is the "histrionic tendency", the taste for a role in the hypnotic session regarded as a dramatic performance. It also appears that a number of hypnotists feel the need to talk a lot. Finally, a motive which seems to play a very important part is the "paradoxical need for simultaneous intimacy and distance" (87, p. 96). The desire to establish such a relationship with another human being is felt by every psychotherapist, but the feeling is strongest in the hypnotist.

It may be concluded that no distinctive traits in the personality of the hypnotist or of the subject have been established which would adequately explain hypnotizability. It is essential, in this type of research, to take the most scrupulous account of the fact that hypnosis is a relationship in which two persons meet and play complementary roles to one another. Hypnotizability therefore depends upon the multiple interpersonal and intrapersonal processes which are activated.

Applications

A DISTINCTION in principle may be made between therapy *by hypnosis* and therapy *under hypnosis*. The former, in the form of short or long sessions, depends upon the curative effect of the hypnotic state itself. The mechanism by which the therapeutic effect is obtained can be interpreted according to the theoretical views of various schools. The Pavlovians refer to prolonged restorative inhibition, the psychoanalysts to regression and instinctual gratification, and finally, an author like J. M. Schultz to a beneficial organismic change of attitude (Umschaltung).

Schilder and Kauders (197) think that "the mental working-through of experiences which takes place during sleep is of importance, in addition to its physical effects" (p. 158).

It is this mental working-through, also known as regression with interpersonal experience, which constitutes, for Gill and Brenman (87), the groundwork on which the psychotherapeutic process operates. It would be possible for this process to be brought about by other means; the hypnotic relationship simply expedites it. But there is nothing specific about it, and for this reason, Gill and Brenman consider that there is no point in using the term "hypnotherapy". Hypnosis is not, for them, a particular kind of psychotherapy, but only something which can play a supporting part in any kind of psychotherapy. This point of view appears on the whole to be well-founded, but several reservations must be made. If we follow Gill and Brenman, we must admit that in prolonged hypnosis, the curative process is entirely due to interpersonal factors. But however important these may be, we cannot, surely, dismiss the *physical* or *psychophysical* value of hypnotic sleep, which has been known since ancient times. Here we have a specific biological piece of behaviour of which animal hypnosis furnishes a simplified model (cf. p. 45). In this case at least, it seems legitimate to talk of hypnotherapy.

Hypnotic sleep prolonged for several days and even for several weeks was used by Janet (104), Wetterstrand (233), Van Renterghem (222) and Schilder and Kauders (197). Russian authors currently use it in prolonged sessions of from one and a half hours to eighteen hours out of twenty-four. Therapeutic suggestions accompany these sessions (43). We are ourselves convinced that the time factor plays a part. We have in fact sometimes obtained results with prolonged sessions when short sessions had been without effect. For the interpersonal and physiological factors to produce their full effects, a certain period of time is necessary.

Sessions of hypnotic sleep with little or no verbal communication are sometimes difficult for the therapist to accept because of their appearance of magic. He is ill at ease in this passive role and feels obliged to talk. On the other hand, it sometimes seems as if the subject, for whom the experience is one of beneficial regression, would rather remain at this non-verbal level.

We have ourselves tried combining drugged sleep with hypnosis. In this treatment, sleep is obtained by doses of drugs at regular intervals. What we did was to replace one of these daily doses by a hypnotic session, which proved just as effective as the drug in maintaining sleep.

An important part of hypnotherapy consists in *direct suggestion oriented towards removal of symptoms;* it is a "covering" therapy aiming at what are called transference cures. The introduction of Freudian psychopathology and the idea of the functional value of the symptom modified psychotherapeutic aims. Psychotherapy became more ambitious, and its aim became the restructuring of the patient's personality. Thus the mere removal of symptoms became of less value because of the appearance of substitute symptoms. Such an attitude may be valuable from a theoretical point of view but sometimes not very useful in practice. Not all patients are capable of the necessary inner effort, and not all can pay the price of restructuring of the personality. Brenman and Gill (34) define the therapeutic effects of direct hypnotic suggestion as follows.

"The therapeutic leverage consists largely of whatever deep unconscious needs are stirred in the patient in his relationship to the therapist during the hypnosis. We do not understand the nature of this relationship, but this does not alter the fact that, by dint of its existence, the patient may obtain relief from his symptoms, sometimes temporarily and often permanently" (34, p. 58).

Kubie and Margolin (125) also present a hypothesis concerning the beneficial effects of the hypnotic relationship. According to them, in the stage of induction, there is a loss of boundaries between hypnotist and subject, while in the hypnotic state the image of the hypnotist is incorporated by the subject. Thus what is involved is "an experimental reproduction of a natural developmental process" (125, p. 621). It might be added that the subject, when he becomes involved in the transference, does not always bring to it purely and simply his own early experience, i.e., does not simply repeat his infantile emotions. If his early experience has been too frustrating, the patient may wish to try for a more gratifying and "reparative" emotional experience. It can be understood that in some exceptional cases (case five, for example), this compensatory aspect may be prevalent. Thus the therapeutic mechanism does not rest exclusively on repression but may involve a process of maturation. We ourselves have found that substitute symptoms do not always appear. Interviews conducted after several years with patients who had been treated in this way sometimes indicated lasting cures or improvements. Even the most direct form of suggestion has a psychotherapeutic context extending beyond it. Complex psychodynamic forces which cannot always be clearly identified are at work in this psychotherapeutic relationship.

Another form of therapy *under hypnosis* is that aimed at *"uncovering"*. Three methods may be distinguished: (1) therapy aimed at the *re-education of attitudes*, (2) *the cathartic method*, (3) *hypnoanalysis*.

1. The first method is often followed by direct suggestions. The insight achieved is still rudimentary. The therapist adopts a persuasive and educative attitude. This method is much used in the U.S.S.R. It combines treatment by "reasoned suggestion" (118) with the "rational psychotherapy" of Dubois (of Berne)* and Déjerine. The physician reinforces direct suggestion with elements of information, explanation and persuasion.

2. The cathartic method is the most famous and the most spectacular. It consists of a discharge of affect due to the reliving of repressed emotions. It still did outstanding service during the Second World War (77, 112, 229) in the treatment of combat neuroses. It does, however, appear to have lost the effectiveness which had formerly been attributed to it, where the neuroses of the civilian population are concerned. It is difficult to decide about it. We do not know for certain whether the results formerly obtained were lasting. It is also possible that modern psychotherapists have less confidence in the method and consequently

---

*The heated controversies at the beginning of the century between Bernheim on the one hand and Dubois on the other are well known. The latter wanted to replace suggestive therapy by persuasive therapy.

use it less effectively. One also finds that the patients today are less inclined to have abreactive experiences. The Russian authors show a dislike for the cathartic method. This attitude appears to be due to the fact that catharsis sets irrational processes in motion and thus falls within the boundaries of psychoanalysis which is rejected in the U.S.S.R. Konstoroum (119, p. 63) admits that the cathartic method has not always been used exclusively by psychoanalysts and does not inevitably have to be interpreted in Freudian terms, but he does not believe in its therapeutic effectiveness. It may, occasionally, facilitate deeper anamnesis, but it must be used with extreme care – the results are not always the right ones and the use of the method may not be without danger for the subject. As a young psychiatrist, who did not use the method, remarked to us in Moscow, "This method puts too much strain on the nervous system of the patient" (or on that of the doctor, as those who favour the psychodynamic approach would feel).

The controversy over who was the first to discover the cathartic method, an honour claimed by both Breuer and Janet, is well known, and we do not intend to discuss it here.

We shall, however, pause for a moment over one point, the interest of which is purely historical (cf. p. 8). It came up in a paper which we found in the course of our research, and concerns "a case of hysterical neurasthenia with double personality" described by Bourru and Burot at the Congress of Hypnotism, 8th to 12th August 1889 (52, pp. 228–40). These authors are known mainly by their book, *Les Variations de la Personnalité* (28)*of 1888 which had been quoted by Janet in *L'Automatisme psychologique* in 1889 (103). In the paper in question, the authors indicate a procedure very similar to the cathartic method. Bourru and Burot again refer to the case which they had already described briefly in their book. Their patient, who was treated about 1887, presented a series of symptoms similar to those of Miss Anna O. They obtained temporary improvements and then cure by hallucinatory revival of certain situations. Although these situations were connected with happy events, the patient nevertheless relived them with quite violent "crises". Improvement followed these attacks. Bourru and Burot regarded this salutary hallucinatory crisis as a treatment of the cause of the illness and not just a treatment of symptoms like direct suggestion. "To combat the morbid phenomena by suggestion," they write, "is not the whole story. These phenomena may disappear while the illness still persists. This is only treatment of symptoms, and is only an expedient. Real and lasting improvement was achieved only when careful observation and logical deduction brought us to the actual origin of the illness . . . These beneficial reactive attacks . . . were above all hallucinations which produced in the patient a severe mental shaking, stirring up the effects associated with the thought which had originally disorganized the brain

---

*This book contains a detailed description of what is today called experimental regression by hypnotic suggestion, a technique used by many contemporary investigators.

and caused the illness." It is stra ge that neither Janet nor Freud, who both registered for the Congress, related this paper to their own knowledge in this field. It appears that Janet spent the whole of 10th August (the day on which the paper concerned was read) at another congress, the Congress of Psychology, about which we shall have more to say. (In particular, he took part in the discussion of Babinski's paper.) Even if he had heard the paper by Bourru and Burot, he might not have given it any particular attention, since it only repeated, though in greater detail, the account which he had already read in *Les Variations de la Personnalité*. If, as is likely, he read the paper later, he does not seem to have been aware of its original contribution, since to the best of our knowledge, he never referred to it.

To find out precisely to what extent Freud participated in the Congress, reference was made to Ernest Jones' recent biography. According to Jones (107, I, p. 198), Freud, together with Bernheim and Liébeault, arrived in Paris at the end of July 1889 from Nancy, to attend the Congress of Hypnotism. Jones writes that Freud was "very bored" with the Congress and left for Vienna again on the evening of 9th August. In that case, Freud could scarcely have had time to be bored. The truth of the matter must be that Jones is mistaken. In fact, Freud was also registered (like Liébeault and Bernheim) as a member of the Congress of Physiological Psychology which took place from 6th to 10th August.* This last conference also included an important section devoted to hypnosis, especially in its psychological aspects, while the Congress of Hypnotism was more concerned with medical problems. Curiously enough, though he had come to Nancy to perfect his technique of hypnosis, Freud showed little interest in the discussions on this subject which took place at the two Congresses, and to which some of the ablest specialists of the time contributed.

Freud left Paris on the evening of 9th August. On the morning of that day, Bernheim had acted as chairman of the Congress of Psychology session, and in the afternoon had given his paper to the Congress of Hypnotism. One may guess that, out of courtesy, Freud did not want to leave before these two meetings. Bourru and Burot gave their paper on the following day. If he had heard it, Freud would perhaps have noted the similarity to the cathartic method as he practised it, following Breuer. He might perhaps have spoken about his own work and that of Breuer and thus cleared up the question of who first discovered the cathartic method.

3.   The boundaries between the cathartic method and hypnoanalysis are fluid. The term *hypnoanalysis*, which occurs sporadically after 1917, first of all referred to a technique which was not content with the removal of symptoms, but aimed at a cure of the source of trouble. It included elements of analysis and insight by cathartic or educative procedures (Hadfield, 91). Its proponents might or might not (Lifchitz, 138) be psychoanalytically oriented. Simmel worked within a psychoanalytic framework. Freud (81)

---

*This was the first International Congress of Psychology. The second, in 1892, changed its name and became the Congress of Experimental Psychology. It was the third, in 1896, which assumed the name of Congress of Psychology (without qualification) which it has retained to the present day. The month of August 1889, which coincided with the Universal Exhibition, was fertile in congresses. There was also the International Congress of Mental Medicine, 5th to 10th August. Some congress members participated in the proceedings of all the three congresses to which we have referred.

refers to him in his *Autobiographical Study* as having used the cathartic method with success in the treatment of war neuroses in the German army during the First World War. Actually, Simmel went further. In addition to cathartic procedures, he made use of analytical sessions and the interpretation of dreams with the patient either awake or under hypnosis. Other authors used similar techniques during the Second World War (77, 112, 229). Today, hypnoanalysis is a technique which combines psychoanalysis and hypnosis. The practical aim of the method is to shorten classical psychoanalysis. Although some authors sometimes limit themselves to a very moderate number of sessions, the average length of hypnoanalytic treatment, according to Brenman and Gill (34) is from 40 to 100 sessions or more.

Two techniques currently in use may be distinguished — a *strictly systematized technique* (R. Lindner) and a *more supple technique* (Erickson, Wolberg, Brenman and Gill, Schneck, Kline and others). All these methods begin with a period of training during which the subject learns to go into a hypnotic state at a given signal. Some authors consider a deep trance necessary for the practice of hypnoanalysis, while others regard a light trance as sufficient. Lindner's method (140) includes two further phases in addition to the training phase. The second phase includes classical psychoanalytic sessions with free association. Hypnosis is used to overcome resistances. When these arise, the patient is hypnotized and the therapist tries to reach the material which the patient could not reveal in the waking state. The treatment ends with a period of re-education and re-orientation during which direct suggestion may actually be used. The second technique is a very flexible one and the authors use a whole range of special techniques for obtaining material — inducing of dreams, regression, automatic writing, imagining of scenes related to the conflict material and so on.

From a theoretical point of view, hypnosis has been reproached with disguising transference and by-passing resistances. The hypno-analysts believe that the processes of defence and resistance are not abolished and that one may work on them and bring about a restructuring of the personality just as in classical psychoanalysis. This technique is at the experimental stage. The accounts published and the results achieved do not justify any definite conclusions about its therapeutic effectiveness; but the

variety of procedures used in the method provide scope for interesting research.

The Problem of Who Should Practise Hypnosis

The same question arises with hypnotherapy as with all kinds of
psychotherapy. Should the right to practise it be restricted to
psychotherapists or allowed to all physicians? The general practitioner is continually engaging in psychotherapy, even if he is
unaware of doing so, since every act of medicine involves an element of psychotherapy. But there has been a growing tendency
to acquaint the general practitioner with psychotherapy so that
he may be aware of what he is doing and so that he may himself
employ the "minor" psychotherapy of everyday practice. But
we doubt whether hypnotherapy can be regarded as a "minor"
kind of psychotherapy. If there is a tendency for it to be regarded
as such, this is because the technique is relatively easy, the results
speedy and deep levels of the personality apparently not reached.
In actual fact, as has already been said, hypnosis is rarely by
itself a form of treatment. Its function is rather to hasten the establishment of the therapeutic relationship and to intensify it.
In analytic terms, it activates powerful processes of transference
and counter-transference which one must be able to handle and
sometimes to stem. It is therefore illogical to regard psychotherapy with hypnosis as easier to conduct than psychotherapy
without hypnosis. We are in full agreement with Rosen when he
says, "No one should ever treat patients on hypnotic levels
for therapeutic goals or with techniques beyond the range of his
usual professional competence with unhypnotized patients"
(191, p. 683). A training in psychotherapy is therefore essential
for anyone wanting to use hypnosis. The general practitioner
may use it in certain cases on condition that he knows something
of psychotherapy. This point of view is accepted in Great Britain.
In the *British Medical Journal* of 8th June 1957, several studies
on hypnosis appear by general practitioners. The conditions for
the practice of hypnotherapy have been defined in the report
of the committee of the American Medical Association set up
for this purpose. The members of this committee take the view
that:

"... a background of psychodynamic psychology and psychiatry is essential in order to understand the phenomena of

hypnosis ... the utilization of hypnotic techniques should be restricted to those individuals who are qualified by background and training to fulfil all the necessary criteria that are required for a complete diagnosis of the illness which is to be treated. Hypnosis should be used on a highly selective basis by such individuals and should never become a single technique used under all circumstances by a therapist" (187, p. 187).

Hypnosis is currently used by dentists in the United States. Some European authors (e.g., Stokvis, 213) are opposed to this use. Here again, from a theoretical point of view, the dentist may be regarded as symbolically affecting deep, unconscious and very vulnerable regions;* and we may wonder whether the patient runs the risk of a traumatic experience. We do not have any large-scale study of patients treated by hypnotist-dentists such as would indicate whether this procedure has any after-effects on the patient's personality. Since the dentist-patient relationship, however, is restricted within close limits, we are perhaps justified in regarding the risk as also limited (provided, of course, that the dentist remains within these limits). Moreover, some American dentists have been turning to modern dynamic psychology in order to become properly aware of these problems. The report of the AMA also lays down conditions for the use of hypnosis by practitioners who are not specialists in psychotherapy.

"No physician or dentist should utilize hypnosis for purposes that are not related to his particular speciality and that are beyond the range of his ordinary competence. As an example, a trained and qualified dentist might use hypnosis for hypnoanaesthesia or hypnoanalgesia or for the allaying of anxiety in relation to specific dental work. Under no circumstances would it be proper for him to use hypnosis for the treatment of neurotic difficulties of his patient. The surgeon, obstetrician, anaesthesiologist, gynecologist, internist or general practitioner may legitimately utilize these techniques within the framework of their own particular field of competence" (*ibid.*).

---

*The specific role of the dentist has been studied by Marie Bonaparte (25). She emphasizes the role of the dentist as "castrator", but also as "restorer of the phallus"; hence the ambivalent transference of the patient in relation to the dental practitioner. R. Held (94) has recently taken up this question again.

Dangers in the Use of Hypnosis

The dangers involved in the use of hypnosis in psychotherapy have been variously regarded. There is in fact no work which meets scientific requirements (control groups, follow-up studies and so on) which would allow an accurate assessment of the disadvantages of hypnosis. But if hypnotherapy involved no risk, its beneficial effects might perhaps be questioned. Assuming that a treatment is not really effective unless it involves some risk, Janet went so far as to "regard it as unfortunate that there is so little danger attaching to the use of hypnotism and suggestion" (105, p. 326).

Any treatment involves risks, and biochemical treatments may actually cause death. Competence is, of course, a primary factor in success, but even experienced specialists may make mistakes which, without causing death, yet have unforeseen results. These are the hazards inherent in any therapeutic procedure.

With the "epidemic" of hypnosis which has been raging in recent years in the United States, voices have been raised pointing out certain harmful effects of hypnotherapy and its possible after-effects. Reporting several cases in which these criticisms are relevant, Rosen expresses the following opinion. "Cases here described show that neither diagnostic uncovering techniques nor supposedly therapeutic chronological regression with abreaction is safe in the hands of persons ignorant of psychodynamics. Failures are as melodramatic as successes" (191).

Hilgard and his collaborators (96) have reviewed the studies which have appeared during recent years on the harmful effects of the use of hypnosis by qualified or unqualified persons. The number of reported cases has risen to fifteen. These are cases in which the suppression of symptoms has led to more severe symptoms, sometimes even to psychotic reactions. "They appear, however," Hilgard *et al.* remark, "chiefly in patients with a long history of illness, and perhaps showing psychotic trends prior to the therapy; there is no way of knowing the total sample from which they are drawn, or to what extent the consequences are determined by ill-advised techniques of psychotherapy rather than with hypnosis as such. Symptom removal by techniques other than hypnosis occasionally has similar consequences" (p. 476).

These authors have themselves experimented on a population of 220 healthy students. They found minor secondary effects, all temporary, in 17 cases (7·7 per cent). In five cases, these effects lasted only a few hours after the experiment. The authors conclude that on the whole, their experimental procedures were innocuous. They found, interestingly enough, that the subjects who showed the secondary effects were those who had unpleasant memories of a chemical anaesthesia which they had previously undergone.

We ourselves take the view that where the suppression of symptoms is concerned, extreme caution is particularly called for if hypnosis is used. Hypnosis does facilitate the suppression of symptoms, but sometimes this may happen too abruptly, with the result not only that more or less severe substitute symptoms may appear, but also that disastrous consequences may ensue which may actually provoke suicidal tendencies in the patient. A preliminary psychiatric assessment is therefore, to repeat, particularly advisable before psychotherapy including hypnosis is used with psychiatric or psychosomatic cases. Whatever precautions may have been taken, however, delicate situations may sometimes arise, and experience of psychotherapy is necessary if the therapist is to be in a position to deal with them. Fortunately, also, the patient of his own accord often takes precautionary measures by assuming a defensive attitude, and when sensing some threat to his personality, may mobilise defences which are adequate for becoming or not becoming involved in the hypnotic relationship.

It may be concluded that hypnotherapy involves risks when it is practised by the unqualified; but that in the absence of statistical evidence, it is difficult to compare these risks with those involved in other treatments. We have ourselves noticed temporary increases in the severity of symptoms of patients given hypnotherapy; but when we saw some of these patients several years later, we found no lasting damage. Admittedly, we did not see all our patients again, but the same is true for the other kinds of therapy.

Hypnosis and Psychoanalysis

FREUD never denied the connexion between hypnosis and psychoanalysis. In particular, he remarks, "It is not easy to overestimate the importance of the part played by hypnotism in the history of the origin of psychoanalysis. From a theoretical as well as from a therapeutic point of view, psychoanalysis has at its command a legacy which it has inherited from hypnotism" (83, p. 192).

The position of hypnosis in analytic psychotherapy was accurately foreseen by Freud himself, who declared in 1918, "It is very probable, too, that the application of our therapy to numbers will compel us to alloy the pure gold of analysis plentifully with the copper of direct suggestion; and even hypnotic influence might find a place in it again, as it has in the treatment of war-neuroses. But whatever form this psychotherapy for the people may take, whatever the elements of which it is compounded, its most effective and most important ingredients will assuredly remain those borrowed from strict psychoanalysis which serves no ulterior purpose" (85, p. 402).

Let us now see under what forms hypnosis may be integrated with analytic psychotherapy. The most ambitious attempt in this direction is represented by hypnoanalysis, the exponents of which believe it to be a form of therapy capable of replacing the standard treatment by shortening it. But as we have said, hypnoanalysis is still at the experimental stage and it would be premature to come to any conclusion about its possibilities. On the other hand, hypnosis may form an ingredient in what are called the "psychoanalytically oriented psychotherapies" (POP). What constitute "psychoanalytically oriented psychotherapies" is not well defined, but three criteria may in principle be borne in mind: (1) the understanding of the symptom in terms of psychoanalytic concepts, (2) the underlying attitude of the therapist toward the patient, which is conditioned by his own personality and his psychoanalytic training (counter-transference), (3) the cautious

64

use, should the occasion arise, of insight into deep-lying conflicts, by the analysis of transference and resistances.

Of these three conditions, the second appears to be by far the most important. Even a very superficial kind of psychotherapy (directive, rational, supportive and so on), if practised by a psychoanalyst and guided by a psychodynamic perspective, should surely be regarded as a "psychoanalytically oriented psychotherapy".

The practitioner must therefore take into account the fact that the hypnotic relationship is characterized by special forms of transference and counter-transference. Because of this, some find the use of hypnosis too distressing. As one of the writer's psychoanalytic teachers remarked, in the hypnotic relationship, "the unconscious of the hypnotist and the unconscious of the patient are in too close contact and this cannot but be exhausting." In conclusion, we should be quite willing to accept the opinion of Kaufman (112), for whom the use of hypnosis is not an anachronism, nor a fixation, nor a kind of regression in relation to modern psychotherapeutic methods, but "does represent a valid modality when applied as a goal-limited psychotherapy within the framework of psychoanalytic psychology" (p. 38).*

There is another point which we should like to raise, which may perhaps explain the diminished effectiveness of hypnosis today compared with last century. Undoubtedly, the therapeutic possibilities of hypnosis were then greatly exaggerated, and scientific rigour in the evaluation of results was lacking. There are, nevertheless, some grounds for believing that last century this form of treatment was more effective. This would at first appear to be due to the fact that the environment at that time was such as to encourage a greater degree of suggestibility; but it is also possible that today we are less well fitted for using hypnosis. It may be that we have less faith in the therapeutic effect, and lose confidence, and that the patient senses this.

A contemporary Soviet author, Kartamishev (111), who uses hypnosis in dermatology, has described excellent results obtained by direct and indirect suggestion in the treatment of warts. But he reports that in the face of the "mocking smiles" of his collaborators, he lost his confidence and his power to heal.

---

*Paper read at the joint meeting of the American Psychiatric Association and the American Psychoanalytic Association, 9th May 1960.

The first practitioners of hypnosis assumed the role of miracle workers and magicians, and this lent itself to abuse. Today we tend to find such an attitude rather amusing. Modern knowledge of psychopathology requires us to adopt a more rational outlook. Awareness of counter-transference likewise leads us to take a more circumspect view. But one may at the same time wonder whether this very caution does not deprive us of a spontaneity which in itself increased our power of suggestion. To this it may be objected that the awareness and control of counter-transference should, on the contrary, allow even more spontaneity. Ideally, the perfect analyst should be able to use any form of psychotherapy, but in our view the problem is too complex for us to draw any general conclusions here.

The discovery and awareness of counter-transference constitutes one of the most important steps in the progress of psychotherapy. It has brought protection for the patient against the unconscious projections of the therapist. The reserve which accompanies it may make some patients feel that they are really being kept at a distance. Indeed, we are sometimes too firmly installed in our neutrality and too lazy to modify this attitude. Modifications are quite permissible in the psychotherapy of psychoses and in the anaclitic treatment of some severe psychosomatic disorders. Margolin (144), who describes an anaclitic treatment necessitating a high degree of gratification on the part of the patient, finds the task so exacting that he actually advises us to have the support of another therapist in this type of treatment. The occasional use of hypnosis might be a useful exercise for any psychotherapist, allowing him to remain adaptable, to vary his attitudes and to avoid becoming too set in his procedures.

Grinberg (89) insists on the need for psychoanalysts to limit the number of hours they devote to the usual kind of treatment; for if they practise this activity exclusively, they are contained within a particular relationship, the psychoanalytic relationship, which in the long run engenders "isolation and deficiency of ordinary communication with others" and "a certain degree of regression". The situation may even lead to "the intensification of persecutory anxieties, with the utilization of schizo-paranoid mechanisms and increased reactions of rivalry, envy, resentment". Grinberg explains in these terms the sharpness and frequency of conflicts between analysts. He admits with Freud "the possibility of awakening instinctive urges, which may have a harmful influence on the analyst's personality because they cannot find an adequate mode of discharge with his patients. At times, in a displaced form – and leading to acting out – the analyst unconsciously chooses a target for discharge. This target is his colleagues" (pp. 362–3). Grinberg advocates as a "mental hygiene" measure the increase of personal contacts involving non-analytic communication – courses, lectures, hospital work and the like. It may be wondered whether, in this connection, communication at the level of hypnosis, which does not involve the rule of strict neutrality for the therapist, might not provide a useful variation for him.

In the same paper, Grinberg refers to Freud and Melanie Klein, compares a good analysis to satisfactory breast-feeding, and emphasizes the gratification which the individual gets from such breast-feeding. This gratification, which is the basis of happiness in later life, makes possible good relations with others.

While we are on the subject of feeding, we may observe that, on a different level, the mother is also "rewarded", for breast-feeding gives her pleasure which is of some importance for her emotional equilibrium and for her capacity for "giving" in the future. If this is so, and if it is agreed that relations between hypnotist and hypnotized are on the oral level (78), the practitioner should gain from such relations the same kind of benefits as the nursing mother.

Karl Menninger (150) considers it valuable for every analyst to devote part of his time to other forms of analytic psychotherapy. Some analysts, however, prefer to confine themselves entirely to the practice of orthodox treatment and therefore stick to the "armchair-couch" setting for the sessions, to use Held's expression (95). Others favour a mode of treatment in which they are face-to-face with their patients (the "armchair-armchair" setting, in Held's terms), in the psychoanalytically oriented psychotherapies. The choice will depend upon the personality of the analyst (and, of course, upon the various factors which may be present in each particular case).

The exclusive practice of hypnotherapy is equally undesirable. According to some psychoanalysts, like the one we have already mentioned (cf. p. 65), the proximity of the unconscious minds of patient and therapist, if prolonged, would constitute a form of emotional stress for the therapist. Again, the use of one single technique may bring other disadvantages, in so far as the psycho-therapist will tend to see more indications for the use of this method and run the risk of applying it in cases more amenable perhaps to a different approach.

Instruction in Hypnosis

HYPNOTIC psychotherapy was taught in France in a number of hospitals at the end of the nineteenth century, and the question of teaching was considered during the 1889 Congress (52). Ladame, a teacher of the University of Geneva, actually proposed a resolution to the effect that hypnosis should be officially introduced into the programmes of psychiatric clinics, and that "the knowledge necessary for the practice of hypnotism as a therapeutic technique should be required of all aspiring to the practice of medicine" (52, p. 38). After some discussion, the Congress unanimously adopted a motion that "It is desirable that the study of hypnotism and its therapeutic applications be introduced into the teaching of medical science" (op. cit., p. 44). This recommendation, however, was never carried out in practice, and remained a dead letter.

In the United States, hypnosis is beginning to be taught in medical schools at both undergraduate and postgraduate levels. The American Medical Association has drawn up a programme for instruction in hypnosis which was discussed in 1960 at a meeting of representatives of 22 medical schools in the United States and Canada (192). The general lines of this programme are as follows:

"1. Training in hypnosis should be based on an understanding of modern psychodynamics and psychopathology, particularly in regard to symptom-formation, the doctor-patient relationship, and the nature of unconscious mental processes.

2. Carefully selected case-material should be used in the training process, with the trainee actually taking responsibility for the treatment of a certain number of cases under supervision.

3. Individual supervision is important throughout, not only for the patient's sake, but for a constant monitoring of the trainee's development and for his maximum utilization of the total educational opportunity.

4. Restrictions should be exercised in the selection of individuals for post-graduate training in hypnosis. They should be screened on the basis of background and previous training, motivation, and their own mental and emotional health and stability.

5. Training in hypnosis is needed at various levels. The program for residents in psychiatry should be more advanced and specialized. However, a good

69

program for undergraduate students may have many facets in common with a good postgraduate program for non-psychiatrists. Some aspects of these two areas of training may profitably be combined."

The American Psychiatric Association has likewise published recommendations on teaching, as follows (183):

"1. Isolated courses limited to the teaching of trance induction techniques are strongly disapproved.

2. The teaching of hypnosis should take place in medical schools and other psychiatric training centres that have an interest in the teaching of hypnosis. When taught in such a climate, where students can acquire adequate knowledge of psychiatric principles, hypnosis may become a useful adjunct to therapy.

3. The teaching of hypnosis should be of sufficient duration and depth for students to acquire adequate understanding of its appropriate place in relation to other psychiatric treatment modalities; of its indications and contraindications; of its values and its dangers. Decisions regarding the depth and extent of the teaching of hypnosis should remain flexible, and should be made by the psychiatric departments teaching such courses.

4. Training in all aspects of hypnosis should be made available to physicians and dentists requesting it.

5. An expansion of the facilities for the teaching of hypnosis is needed particularly at the postgraduate level. The establishment of postgraduate courses in medical schools and other teaching centres under the direction of the department of psychiatry is recommended.

6. Physicians practising hypnosis should do so only in their particular field of medical competence.

7. The need for continued study of hypnosis and for adequate research is emphasized, with particular reference to delineating its place in the total treatment program."

Important research projects, as well as teaching, are currently in progress. Grants amounting to a million dollars have been made available for research by various institutions in the United States (192).

Kennedy, the late Professor of Psychological Medicine in the University of Edinburgh, considers that hypnosis may have a useful function to perform in training for psychotherapy (114, 1957). "From the point of view of education in psychotherapy," he writes, "we were able with the aid of hypnosis to present to the trainee an elementary version of the relationships of physician and patient which may occur in the therapeutic situation and of the ways in which these can be manipulated to the patient's advantage" (p. 1317).

In addition to the practice of hypnosis, the future psychotherapist will learn the theory and may from this pass to more complex forms of therapy. Later, he will decide whether to undergo a personal analysis. Kennedy adds, "Such a progression could be regarded as a recapitulation of the way in which Freud and many others, beginning with hypnosis and learning its valuable lessons, eventually found the way to other methods" (*ibid.*). Other authors do not share this opinion. There are some who would rather recommend the reverse of this procedure, i.e., that one should first become familiar with dynamic psychotherapy, then undergo a training analysis and move to hypnosis last. The latter procedure would seem to us preferable, particularly if it is desired to use hypnosis as an agent of deep psychotherapeutic inquiry.

Indications

THE statement of the American Psychiatric Association (183) summarizes, as follows, the conditions for the therapeutic use of hypnosis. "Hypnosis is appropriately and properly used in the course of therapy only when its employment serves therapeutic goals without posing undue risks to the patient. With selected patients, it can be used for sedative, analgesic and anaesthetic purposes; for the relief of apprehension and anxiety; and for symptom suppression. It can also be used, but on a still more highly selective basis, as an adjunct in the treatment of patients with neurotic or psychotic illness."

It is difficult to define precise limits to the therapeutic indications for hypnosis. These will depend more on the patient than on the disease. The therapist will obviously be guided by the diagnosis in attempting treatment using hypnosis, but at the same time, he must not forget that the same diagnosis does not always mean the same reaction to hypnotherapy. Among the patients who are chosen for hypnosis, some are automatically eliminated by the fact that they cannot be hypnotized. The patient who is hypnotizable shows that he is accessible to psychotherapy. It is at least worth trying. This does not mean that it will always be successful; but the patient, when he accepts the hypnotic relationship, is, as it were, holding out a hand to the physician. It is for the latter to use this situation to the patient's best advantage.

We ourselves, in choosing the patients with whom to use hypnotherapy, were initially guided by practical considerations. We were looking for a form of treatment which could be applied to the patients within a short period. Among these patients were some who were inaccessible to depth-therapy because of the inadequacy of their dynamic resources. Others would not accept any treatment of long duration. For some, hypnosis was the only possible therapeutic method, and sometimes represented a form of emergency treatment. It may also be the case that patients

72

treated by hypnosis for an acute episode are then more favourably disposed toward some other form of psychotherapy.

Treatment was seldom entirely limited to direct suggestion under hypnosis. In most cases, this was accompanied by psychotherapeutic talks under hypnosis or in the waking state, the patient sitting opposite the therapist or lying down, sometimes able to see the therapist and sometimes not. Sometimes we used the cathartic method and specialized techniques such as regression, induced dreams and so on, the specialized techniques being used more for investigation than for therapy. We must now admit that, like every psychotherapist, we have our own particular theoretical outlook. We employ the psychoanalytic frame of reference and regard the hypnotic relationship as a form of psychotherapy accompanied by a special kind of situation involving transference and counter-transference, of which we always try to remain aware. As in any psychoanalytically oriented therapy, "insight" or "working through", if one tackles it, must be handled with care.

Evaluation of results requires extreme caution. The difficulties of evaluation in any kind of psychotherapy are well known. None can boast of having demonstrated its effectiveness in clear-cut quantitative terms. Moreover, and this is perhaps the most serious deficiency, generally speaking, in the publications on the subject, sufficient time has not elapsed for us to be able to estimate the real worth of the successes obtained. Thus, during the great period of hypnosis, there was a mass of unconfirmed claims of therapeutic success. They cured everything. And even today, papers err in the same way; there are insufficient studies covering a reasonable follow-up period. Last, but not least, there is a major difficulty, the still controversial question of the criteria of cure, which is as relevant to hypnosis as to other forms of psychotherapy.

It appears very probable that the therapeutic results obtained by hypnosis last century were better than those obtained today. It is, of course, difficult to get comparable figures. Follow-up studies carried out after a sufficient period of time were rare (as indeed they still are today). The older writers, moreover, did not perhaps pay sufficient attention to substitute symptoms. Nevertheless, if we confine our observations to the most responsible of these authors, we certainly get the impression that their hypnotic treatments were more effective and were used for disorders which today are much less amenable to this form of therapy. If we read the Proceedings of the two International Congresses (52, 53), we find, for example, positive results reported (after an apparently reasonable time) for certain cases of agoraphobia, obsessional neurosis and writer's cramp (De Jong,

52, pp. 196–261). Hypnotherapy appeared to be especially effective in the treatment of addictions.

Comparative studies of the results of different kinds of psychotherapy have been attempted. There is, for example, the work of Stokvis (214), which represents an effort at statistical evaluation of psychotherapeutic results by means of a follow-up inquiry carried out from six months to five years after treatment. The author himself draws attention to the methodological difficulties which he encountered, and the validity of his conclusions must be regarded as strictly relative. He takes the social adjustment of the patient as the criterion of result, and distinguishes two forms of therapy, "covering" ("Zudeckende") and "uncovering" ("Aufdeckende"). The former, which includes suggestive procedures, is a superficial form of therapy. The latter is a form of depth therapy with insight and expression, which includes analytic treatment (Individual Psychology). The therapeutic results obtained with the two methods appear to be about the same. The treatment of psychoneuroses gave from 5 to 10 per cent of good results (seventy-five cases treated by superficial therapy and thirty by depth therapy), 40 per cent of moderate results, 25 per cent of doubtful results and 25 per cent of failures. Positive results were slightly higher for psychosomatic disorders. The average length of the treatments was twenty-five sessions spread over 5·3 months for the superficial therapy and one hundred sessions spread over 4·5 months for the depth therapy. The two groups consisted of patients with comparable diagnoses.

We shall now review the disorders in which an attempt has been made to apply hypnosis. As a form of psychotherapy, hypnosis has been tried in all disorders, organic or functional, in which there is an emotional element, whether this is in the etiology or in the course of the illness. Our observations fall into three sections, (a) psychosomatic medicine, (b) psychiatry, (c) miscellaneous. In the first section, we shall use the divisions traditionally related to the various systems. We shall have occasion to mention certain syndromes which are purely organic but where psychotherapeutic help may be beneficial in relation to the functional or subjective aspect of the disease. It need scarcely be said that our list makes no claim to be exhaustive.

We shall give in more detail some fairly straightforward case histories, which we were able to follow up over a relatively long period, selected from various fields. These do not always show clear-cut overall success. It is not denied that, in cases where positive results were obtained, some other form of psychotherapy might also have proved effective. But hypnosis does seem to have made a valuable contribution.

(a) Psychosomatic Medicine

Cardio-vascular system. Arterial hypertension has been treated by Russian authors by means of prolonged sessions, going so far as to become veritable prolonged sleep treatments (43).

Cardiac neurosis with arrhythmia may also benefit from hypnotherapy. And finally, in patients suffering from angina pectoris or cardiac infarction or myocarditis, hypnosis is useful in inducing tranquillity and reducing anxiety.

Respiratory system. The precise etiology of asthma is not known, but it is known that an emotional element is involved along with the allergic factors. All treatments are symptomatic. Hypnosis may bring improvement and may constitute an emergency treatment in *status asthmaticus* (206). An American author (112) reports five cases of patients in the *status,* for whom hypnosis represented a vital safeguard, allowing them to breathe normally.

Endocrine system. Attempts have been made, in cases of obesity, to reduce appetite and establish a diet by direct suggestion. Subjects thus treated were able to lose weight. But it must be added that the etiology of obesity includes important psychological aspects needing appropriate psychotherapeutic management.

CASE 1.

Miss O . . . , 23 years of age, a medical student, was referred to us on 12th March 1958 by an endocrinologist. She was suffering from oliguria, which obliged her "to suffer the pangs of thirst and hunger so as not to become of monstrous dimensions". According to our colleague, this was probably a case of hypersecretion of anti-diuretic hormones, possibly of a psychogenic nature. In addition, the patient was in a state of marked depression and was unable to work. We learned that she had been obese and oliguric since the age of ten years. When we saw her, she weighed 132 pounds for a height of five feet three inches, which is not excessive, but she had fixed a weight of 106 pounds for herself. She had curtailed her drinking and followed a Draconian regime – 600 to 700 calories per day for several years. From time to time she was overcome by hunger and let herself go, and might put on up to nine pounds per day, which she tried to lose again by taking massive doses of purgatives. Two years previously, she had started on a course of psychotherapy which she had discontinued after two sessions. The year after this, she had undertaken psychoanalytic treatment which she had broken off after three months. For a year, her emotional failures had been accumulating in a complex way which we cannot describe here. The whole picture was of a personality with many conflicts, which was resistant to any psychotherapeutic procedures. She insisted upon the organic origin of her troubles and refused any form of analytic treatment.

We faced an emergency. Since the possibilities were limited, we decided to use hypnosis in an attempt to reduce the symptoms. We adopted a "planning" strategy to support her in preparing for an examination which she had failed the previous year, and in which she was particularly anxious to succeed this time, since she could not take it again after another failure. We had no hope of achieving any modification of the personality structure for the time being, but we felt that we might be able to make some move in the direction of depth therapy later on. A hypnotic state was induced and she proved to be a good subject. The effect of the first session, at which she was given post-hypnotic suggestions, was remarkable. She began to urinate normally. The pangs of hunger had stopped and after the second session (about seven days later) she had lost nine pounds. She weighed 119 pounds, exactly the weight which had been suggested to her. She also began to work again and to prepare for her examination. Having got over the acute phase of her disorder, the patient feared a relapse. She went into a nursing home which she left again after three days. She broke off treatment with us. From the news which we had of her from time to time, we learned that she had ups and downs, but that she had been able to work and had succeeded in passing her examinations.

This patient was seen again in September 1962. She had finished her studies and was practising gynecology. She had not got married, which she regretted. She was on a diet, but the question of her weight no longer obsessed her. She still had her conflicts. She had tried treatment by narco-analysis without success. She was still opposed to depth therapy.

Gastro-intestinal system. Gastric or duodenal ulcer is treated by prolonged sessions (a kind of rest-cure, inspired by sleep therapy). Hypnosis may also be used for spasms of the oesophagus and cardia. Constipation and diarrhoea have been experimentally influenced by suggestion. Hypnotherapy may also have application in gastro-enterology, where there is pain and vomiting. These symptoms, when they appear in ulcer patients, may precipitate a decision to operate before the possibilities of medical treatment have been fully explored. These gastrectomized patients will retain the same symptoms after the operation and require psychotherapeutic treatment. Finally, hypnosis has been used in ulcerative colitis.

CASE 2.

Mr. Bar..., 31 years of age, an electrician, married and the father of four children, was first treated by us in June 1953. We saw him at the gastro-enterology clinic at the Institut Gustave-Roussy, where he was treated for gastric disorder with vomiting, pain, and considerable emaciation. He had had a gastrectomy in 1952 following a hematemesis during a painful attack. The operation revealed neither duodenal nor gastric ulcer, but the section was quite close to the pylorus. Since 1944, the patient had had gastric trouble with vomiting and pain. The operation relieved the patient for two months, and then the attacks started again, becoming progressively more violent. The patient became unable to work. Another operation was performed two months later for adhesions. There was another improvement lasting for a month, when the same kind of trouble started again. The general condition of the patient was affected. He had lost 48 pounds in weight during the previous eighteen months, walked with a stick and had not worked for several months.

Our examination of the patient, and in particular his own description of his symptoms aroused our suspicions. He compared his pain to a spider moving and putting out tentacles in the pit of his stomach. He thought he had cancer. We felt that this was a case of hysterical personality structure without any chance of insight. Moreover, blindness of the left eye, the result of a wound received during a bombardment, was discovered. The ophthalmologist consulted had noticed the scar, but considered that it did not justify the blindness, which would thus be of a hysterical nature. We decided to use hypnosis along with active psychotherapy aimed at enabling the patient to return to work. The patient proved to be a good subject, but attended the sessions very irregularly, having a very ambivalent attitude toward treatment. There was, however, a relief of symptoms and the patient put on weight.

We used prolonged hypnotic sessions at the start, but then decided to try an investigation under hypnosis, aimed at catharsis, even although we realized that the personality structure was precarious. The patient was asked to re-live the scene of the famous bombardment in which he had been wounded. As soon as he started to recall this, he suddenly came out of the trance in a fit of panic. We calmed him down and decided, in view of his fragility, to have recourse to a compromise. From this time on, we elected to alleviate his digestive troubles and to leave aside for the time being the solution of the blindness. This position appears to have allowed an improvement in both his gastric condition and his general health and thus facilitated a return to social and professional life. The patient was able to carry on this life satisfactorily for two years. In July 1956, he carried on his work while complaining moderately of his physical condition. In May 1958, he was enjoying continued good health. He no longer vomited. His family had increased by a fifth child. His material situation had improved, and he had succeeded in leaving the slum where he had been living to move to a council flat.

Here we have a patient whom treatment preserved from the chronic invalidism and social downfall for which he was heading. The hypnotic relationship, with its instinctual gratification (without going into all the psychodynamic mechanisms) appears to have allowed a mobilization of resources and a partial cure.

The emergence from the trance during the cathartic session might be taken as an illustration of the observations of Brenman, Gill and Knight on the fluctuations in the depth of trance as an ego function. Confronted with a situation seen as a threat, the patient wakes up.

We saw this patient again in August 1962. He had lost a son of 15 years of age from leukemia and had a reactive depression. In order to help him, we attempted to hypnotize him but he proved resistant.

Genito-urinary system. Although the first book written along psychosomatic lines was published (1925) by a urologist (203), urology is a neglected field in psychosomatics (just as in psychoanalytic literature the urethral area is a kind of "poor relation" of the anal area).

An irritable bladder is a very common and well-established syndrome which in French medical terminology has a well-established designation, *cystalgie à urines claires*. It is characterized by pain and frequency. It has been studied more frequently in female than in male patients, although it occurs in both sexes (the frequency symptom, however, occurring predominantly in female patients). To the best of our knowledge, no important work on this as a psychosomatic problem has been published in English, although the present writer and his collaborators (50) recognized it as a psychosomatic condition.* This urological disorder tends to be chronic. If caught at the start, it can be influenced by hypnotic therapy. Intervention is more uncertain when the disorder has become chronic, as is true of any therapy. Certain of these cases take the form of genuine psychotic disturbances which do not respond to hypnotherapy. It is easier to effect relief of the pain than to improve the frequency. If professional life can be maintained, the prognosis is more favourable, as is true of any other therapy.

In the psychotherapy of psychogenic urinary retention, hypnosis proves to be a very valuable aid, generally giving positive results.

In post-pubertal enuresis, hypnosis, in our opinion, constitutes the most satisfactory treatment. We have treated about fifty cases, very often with good results. We have applied to the treatment of enuretics a technique which we call "psychotherapy on demand". There is no fixed schedule. The amount of time between sessions is variable, the patients asking for an appointment when they want to or when they feel the need to do so. We found with our cases that improvement was progressive. Cure was achieved in general several months after treatment began, and sometimes some time after the last session. This form of treatment is very instructive on how hypnotherapy works in these cases, even although it is not accompanied by insight. We got the impression that a process of progressive maturation was going on and the patients came for treatment when their impulse-defence balance allowed them. Several years have now elapsed and we have seen no signs of substitute symptoms.

Stress incontinence is regarded as an organic disorder calling for surgical treatment. We know of one case, however (Case 5), in which the patient was cured by hypnosis. The cure has now been maintained for several years (1).

Some American authors (24) applied hypnosis for analgesic purposes in 200 cases involving the following operations: urethral dilatation in adults and children; cystoscopy and catheterization of the ureters; fulguration of small vesical tumours; urethral meatotomy; catheterization of the bladder and cystography,

---

*An account of this paper may be found in the *Encyclopedia of Urology* (5).

especially in children; and so on. They used hypnosis in some cases where the patients were unable to void while a cysto-urethrogram was being made; these patients were able to void when the examination was repeated after they had been hypnotized.

Hypnotic suggestion may sometimes constitute an emergency treatment. There is, for example, the case of a doctor's young fiancée, who suffered from pelvic pains with severe frequency. The bride-to-be was afraid that a dire necessity would interrupt the marriage ceremony. She was hypnotized and reassured the day before the civil ceremony, which passed off uneventfully. Unfortunately, the young woman did not come back to us again, and a fortnight later, in the middle of the church ceremony, she had to absent herself to attend to a pressing need.

Disturbances of sexual potency in men and frigidity in women in general require deep psychotherapy. Results have, however, been obtained in certain cases of male impotency with shorter treatment of which hypnosis formed a part. We have treated in this way several young subjects who were well-adjusted to work and social life and who had become impotent when they became engaged. Their partners were apparently not neurotic. A few hypnotic sessions combined with invigorating psychotherapy were sufficient to obtain positive results, which were maintained several years later.

In gynecology, menstrual periods have been made to appear and disappear experimentally by hypnosis. This fact has been put to good use in disorders relating to menstruation and the menopause, and in vaginismus.

CASE 3.

Mrs. Le G . . . , 56 years of age, married, was hospitalized for cystitis with hematuria from 7th to 22nd August 1952 at the Argenteuil hospital. The cystitis was alleviated by the usual treatment, but the patient was observed to be suffering from chronic urinary retention with overflow, the residual urine in the bladder varying from 800 to 1,000 c.c. and even more. It appeared that this chronic urinary retention was already well-established, which would explain the distention of the bladder. The patient was referred, on 22nd September 1952, to the Hôpital Saint-Louis, for further investigation. The usual examinations were made, followed by a neurological examination which turned out to be negative. It was then thought that a very old bladder neck contracture might be the cause of the trouble. This might in fact have explained the residual urine but not the complete urinary retention. An emotional trauma was suspected and the patient was referred to us for a psychosomatic examination, which was made on 1st December 1952. The case was one of an unsophisticated woman who, at the time we saw her, was suffering from severe frequency (with overflow), and burning sensations in the bladder which made her incapable of working and impaired her general state of health. She seemed to us to be a person of great goodwill and very anxious to be cured. She reacted remarkably to hypnosis. After several sessions, she urinated 200 c.c. by herself, then about 400 c.c., although there was still some residual urine.

Her general condition improved. She resumed work two months after the beginning of treatment. Since she still had 500 c.c. residual urine because of the chronic organic bladder distention, and since this residual urine was a potential source of infection, the question of an operation was raised. The patient had always been opposed to a surgical operation, but she now accepted it. The operation was performed in October 1953. After the operation, we again employed hypnosis for post-operative sedation in order to avoid the usual sedative drugs. Afterwards she still had some slight residual urine, but was otherwise very well. She was seen again at regular intervals. In May 1958, the residual urine was 400 c.c., but the patient experienced no discomfort and was socially extremely well adjusted. When she was seen again in September 1962, her residual urine was 300 c.c. An operation was suggested. She was hesitant but in the end agreed.

In this case, the patient had a chronic organic disorder. On top of the organic disorder, there was a functional disturbance in the form of total urinary retention, which may have been precipitated by the patient's conflicts with her sister. This led to her giving up work. Hypnotherapy had quite rapid beneficial effects on the patient's physical condition and morale and retrieved her socially. Despite this improvement, however, her residual urine remained a constant danger and she had to be kept under supervision. A second surgical operation under favourable psychological conditions became possible. This case emphasizes the danger of possibly suppressing a functional symptom without taking account of the organic context. It is with this type of patient that the harm done by quacks is greatest.

CASE 4.

Mr. Mok ... was a patient from the urology department of the Hôpital Saint Louis. He began to have trouble with his urine in 1943 while a prisoner of war, at the age of 26, in the form of frequency and enuresis. In 1950, he was suffering from dysuria, with residual urine of about 250 c.c. and with dilatation of the upper urinary ways. The frequency necessitated micturition almost every half hour. The urine was very cloudy. Treatment with silver nitrate in July 1950 provoked an attack of urinary retention which required catheterization lasting for two days. This urinary retention was followed by a feverish state lasting for three days, with a temperature of 104 degrees. An endoscopic resection of the bladder neck was performed on 22nd July 1950. The frequency became even greater, and obliged the patient to keep a bottle beside him during the night. The patient returned to the department on 31st October 1950. He was suffering from extreme frequency (every five minutes), burning sensations, cloudy urine and residual urine of 200 c.c., and enuresis. His general condition was much deteriorated. A second endoscopic resection of the prostate was performed on 2nd October 1954. He left hospital on 11th October 1954, but his symptoms did not disappear. He was again hospitalized on 11th July 1955, with diurnal and nocturnal frequency (he had to get up seven times during the night) and enuresis. He was referred to us on the 9th of the following August.

He was a park-attendant with a rather unsophisticated personality. For this reason, psychological examination proved difficult. Hypnosis appeared to be the only treatment possible and he reacted favourably. The frequency decreased considerably. After three months, he had to get up only twice during the night. He put on weight and had no other subjective symptoms, and was able to resume work. We saw him again in May 1958, about two and a half years after treatment had stopped. The improvement had been maintained. He had gained nearly two stones in weight and no longer suffered with his bladder, although he still had 70 c.c. residual urine. In September 1962 his condition was unchanged.

Here we have a patient with an organic disease who exaggerated his symptoms for emotional reasons which we were not able to discover. Treatment allowed him to resume a normal existence, although the organic basis of the disease remained unchanged.

Case 5.*

Mrs. Bo . . . , 24 years of age, married and mother of one child, was hospitalized at Lariboisière on 15th April 1958, for stress incontinence. Since childhood, the patient had been incontinent when she coughed, exerted herself or ran, but had been continent when standing or when lying down. She had had several surgical operations, but her troubles were always accentuated after these. In 1955 she had a bilateral ovarian excision. After this operation, incontinence began to occur when she walked quickly and even when she was standing. On 25th January 1957, she had a subtotal hysterectomy, after which her incontinence was almost continuous, complete in the standing position and a little less when she was lying down. On 8th November 1957, she had a plication of the bladder neck (Kelly's operation). There was no improvement. On 19th January 1958, she had a cervicocystopexy. After this operation, her incontinence was almost complete and rendered any activity impossible. Nocturnal enuresis also appeared. Such was her condition on admission to hospital.

The possibility of a further operation was raised, but before a decision was taken, the patient was referred to us for examination. It had been observed that since she had entered the Department, the nocturnal incontinence had disappeared. During the day, she was able to control micturition to a certain extent. We examined her on 24th April. The patient had had an unhappy childhood and had experienced numerous emotional frustrations. There was a psychiatric background – her father had died from delirium tremens and her grandmother had been certified. She was completely frigid. She seemed to be suggestible and proved to be a good hypnotic subject. On the evening of the hypnotic session, she wet her bed, but was not to do so again up to her release on 26th April. She no longer suffered from incontinence during the day. She left hospital and was then treated as an out-patient. During the week following her release from hospital, she wet the bed several times at night but had no stress incontinence. Several weeks later she no longer had any trouble.

In the light of the demonstration of the importance of the emotional factor in this patient's illness, it was decided to postpone a more radical operation. We saw the patient again on 22nd July. She informed us that she had had no trouble, either during the day or at night, for six weeks. Her habitual irritability had, however, increased (without yet reaching disturbing proportions) and she said that she sometimes felt like "breaking everything". But she added that she still preferred these fits of rage to her urinary troubles. It is possible that a substitution mechanism was involved, urethral aggression being transformed into psychological aggression. But the latter, in the circumstances, was a less severe handicap. Psychodynamic equilibrium was "satisfied" with a minor personality symptom in place of the somatic symptom, and thus allowed a return to social

*Cf. (1).

life with the cathexes which this involved. The patient was seen again on 6th October, when she had no more urinary trouble and her fits of rage were less serious. She stopped coming for treatment. When seen again on 14th April 1959, Mrs. Bo ... had no urinary trouble and had resumed work, which had been interrupted for several years. In September 1962 her condition was unchanged. There was clearly no longer any question of a surgical operation.

*Obstetrics.** It is well known that hypnosis played a role of the first importance in the development of the psychoprophylactic method of preparation and conduct of childbirth, which is used on a large scale in many countries today. The beneficial effect of hypnosis on labour pains and even on the rhythm of the uterine contractions has been known for a century. Hypnosis may be used either during both preparation and labour (the woman being delivered under hypnosis), or only during preparation, in which case the analgesic effect is obtained by post-hypnotic suggestion, the woman being delivered in the normal waking state. The hypno-suggestive method also has favourable effects on the physiology of pregnancy and labour.

Hypnotic analgesia provided a starting-point for the Soviet founders of the psychoprophylactic method, to whom it proved the reality of verbal analgesia. They abandoned it because it could not be applied on a large scale (on account of lack of trained practitioners, reticence and so on), and replaced it with non-hypnotic didactic, physiotherapeutic and psychotherapeutic methods. They still, however, use hypnosis as an additional help in difficult cases — when the women are particularly anxious, when they are suffering from pyelitis of pregnancy or from cardio-vascular disorders, and in difficult confinements.

The hypno-suggestive method also continues to be used side by side with the psychoprophylactic method in ordinary cases in the Soviet Union (239), where there are a few "hypnotariums" (218, 223) for collective preparation. It is likewise used in other countries (14), particularly in the United States, where some practitioners combine it with didactic and physiotherapeutic measures (51,122). We ourselves, in our experiments with this technique, have obtained satisfactory results in relation to labour pains and lumbar pains during pregnancy. Other practitioners are now beginning to apply the method in France (90).

The influence of hypnosis on the vomiting of pregnancy has

*For a detailed treatment, see the present writer's book on this subject (48).

been well known for a century. The Russians also use it in eclampsia.

Dermatology. Skin diseases have been the object of many applications of hypnotherapy. Two Soviet authors have even devoted books to the problem (106, 111). In another book, by an American author (163), devoted to the study of emotional factors in diseases of the skin, hypnosis has a place among the kinds of therapy used. The influence of hypnosis on warts, which are benign tumours of virus origin, is well known. When the mechanism of this is properly understood, we shall undoubtedly have taken a considerable step towards understanding the relation between body and mind. Nothing illustrates better the importance of the interpersonal factor than the following story, reported by one author. In a clinic where warts were treated by suggestion, the percentage of successes was directly proportional to the importance of the duties performed by the practitioners, the professor obtaining the most successes.

Warts on the hands may sometimes represent a social handicap for young women, as in the case of a student of 17 years of age treated by us. A large number of warts had appeared at the age of twelve, when she had stopped biting her nails. Homeopathic treatment and diathermy had been ineffective. The patient refused to go out because of her disorder. The progressive disappearance of the warts began after the first hypnotic session (she had two in all). At the end of several weeks her hands were clear. Two years later her hands are still clear. This cure had marked repercussions on the young woman's social life.

Many other studies have demonstrated the action of suggestion in diseases of the skin. In the older literature, there is the famous experiment in which second-degree burns were produced by suggestion (though recent authors do not seem to be able to repeat these results). Similarly, the appearance of labial herpes has been induced. Some results have been obtained in the treatment of eczema, psoriasis, urticaria, alopecia and neurodermatitis. Since the etiology of these disorders is still obscure, all treatments, including hypnosis, are symptomatic and relapses are to be expected. In published results, the continuation of the improvement has not been confirmed a sufficiently long time after the disappearance of the symptom. We have ourselves treated three cases of psoriasis and obtained a clear skin. In one case, there was a relapse after some time, while in another the clear skin remained after three years. We did not see the third patient again. An English author (146) reports spectacular results in a case of the congenital ichthyosiform erythrodermia of Brocq, in which the cure was maintained after several years. He also mentions, following other writers, certain rare congenital dermatological diseases treated successfully by hypnosis, namely congenital pachyonychia and congenital linear naevus. A Soviet author (174) reports a serious case of herpes gestationis cured by hypnosis.

Central Nervous System. Hypnotherapy has been applied to insomnia, headaches and backaches. The last two of these do not in general react readily to suggestive therapy. Very deep regression is involved. Paradoxically, it is easier to influence organic pains. This indicates caution in these cases where the pain represents a warning-signal which should not be obscured.

Parkinsonism and multiple sclerosis have likewise been attacked with a view to reducing the intensity of the symptoms. Several authors also report success in the treatment of stammering and tics. These last results seem to be well founded when the disorders are of a hysterical nature; but they must be regarded with reserve in other cases.

Dentistry. Dentists have always given the greatest attention to the problem of anaesthesia (we owe the use of ether as an anaesthetic to a dentist). Today they are using hypnosis for painful operations as well as to calm the anxiety of patients who do not tolerate dental work well. Again, hypnosis may be of use with patients with intractable nauseous reflexes when anything is introduced into their mouths.

Case 6.

We treated Mr. Ba ... in 1956. He was a man of 64 years of age, married, who had been sent to us by a dentist. He was a hyperactive, big-business-man type, with a robust appearance. For fifteen years, however, he had suffered from arrhythmia. A practised gourmet and a member of a gastronomic club, he had had a gastrectomy five years previously.

The oral region appeared to occupy a prominent position in his life. This man had always had great difficulties with dentists. The smallest foreign body introduced into his mouth, such as a mirror or a roll of cotton wool, provoked violent nauseous reflexes. He was even afraid to use a toothbrush. He began to lose his teeth and the question of a prosthesis arose. The dentist faced two problems — doing the preparatory work and carrying out the prosthesis. He thought that with adequate medication he could, at a pinch, manage the preparatory work, but did not believe that his patient could tolerate the prosthesis once the effect of the pre-medication had worn off. Several times the operation had to be put off. The periodontosis from which the patient was suffering was advancing rapidly and the situation was becoming very serious. At this point, the practitioner, having no other means of coping with the situation, thought of hypnosis and sent the patient to us. We made a preliminary assessment. The patient was sceptical about the results of treatment by suggestion. Accordingly, after deciding to associate him actively with the treatment, we coached him in auto-hypnosis which he was also to practise at home. We also confirmed that he had a need to retain his impressive bearing and his capacity for gastronomic satisfaction.

After several preparatory sessions, he was advised to let the dentist start work. The latter started by taking an impression. Wanting to take no chances in obtaining a good impression, he prescribed drugs to be taken for three days (barbiturate morning and night and phenergan on retiring), and all went well. A second session with us preceded the extractions and the insertion of a temporary denture which the patient was able to keep in. The rest of the operation—the extraction of the lower teeth and the fitting and insertion of the permanent denture—was accomplished without difficulty, this time without the help of drugs. The patient was able to tolerate everything and his difficulties had apparently disappeared. We have heard that he has continued in good health.

It was clearly tempting to seek for the underlying cause of this patient's anxiety, but in view of his age and the urgency of his condition, we abandoned an investigation in depth. We played upon his need for mastery by making him take an active part in the treatment. We made it possible for him to have his operation, whatever the symbolic significance of it may have been.

Pediatrics. The hypnotizability of children is a controversial subject. Some authors think that children are less hypnotizable than adults but more suggestible. A Dutch author (213) recommends that the child's environment should be well known and, if the father is tyrannical, that a very gentle method of hypnosis should be used. Hypnosis is used for enuresis and for various hysterical symptoms—paralysis, blindness, deafness and so on.

(b) Psychiatry

Hysteria. Hysteria has often been regarded as a disorder peculiarly suited to hypnotherapy. The disorder no longer appears in the same forms as it used to. Major hysterical fits are scarcely ever seen now. But this does not mean that hysteria has disappeared. Clinically, without going into theoretical or nosological questions, it may be said that it can assume a serious form leading either to severe (or even borderline) neuroses, or to certain serious functional disorders. These two categories are not amenable to hypnotherapy and seem to be very resistant to any form of psychotherapy.

Another less serious category which is amenable to hypnotherapy is represented by the multiple conversion neuroses —
paralysis, dysphagia, aphonia, amnesia (Case 7), stammering and
so on, or by subjects with a hysterical personality suffering from
minor functional disorders.

Case 7.*

Mrs. Su..., 34 years of age, married with one little boy, was hospitalized at
Villejuif on 28th October 1949, with hysterical amnesia consequent upon a
series of shocks including the death of her father and her involvement in an
abortion by a friend whom she agreed to help. There was a loss of memory for
a period of twelve years. The illness had been preceded by a depressive period
in which the patient took massive doses of cerebral stimulant, and it had apparently
been precipitated by the film, *The Snakepit*.† The history showed a family
incidence of somnambulism and "nerves". During interview, the patient told
us she was 21 years of age, and did not appear to recognise either her husband
or her son. Her general condition was depressive. Under hypnosis, she told us
the events which took place during the period for which she had lost her memory.
Before she came out of the trance, we suggested to her the re-integration of this
period. Emergence from the trance state was accompanied by emotional expressions of joy at being delivered from her distressing state. A few hypnotic sessions
together with supportive psychotherapy acted in a generally stimulating way and
the depression disappeared. The patient was able to leave hospital and resume
work. When we saw her again after four years, she was in good health and well
adjusted. Later, she failed to answer a request to attend, but did appear, on
request, in September 1962. She had been suffering from asthma for a year,‡
and had been attended by a physician in the town. She was not very keen on the
hypnotic treatment which was proposed.
In this case, we have a clearly hysterical disorder in a hypnotizable and otherwise well-adjusted subject. Unlike severe hysterics, she proved amenable to
psychotherapy. She was the first patient whom we had hypnotized in fifteen years,
and it was perhaps her good response which revived our interest in this field.

Anxiety neurosis. This is characterized by a state of chronic
anxiety with occasional acute exacerbations. In such cases,
hypnotherapy can be of service in calming acute anxiety and in
allowing an approach to be made to the patient's situation and
its conflict-engendering problems.

Phobias. These really call for classic psychoanalytic treatment. Some writers who have treated phobias by hypnoanalysis

---

*Cf. (154).

†A well-known film in which the action took place in a mental hospital.

‡Patients do not always come when requested. In general, they come when
they need help, although they do not always accept it. Socio-economic level
is also significant, patients from the lower levels being more likely to appear
(Cases 3 and 4).

regard their operations as being of the nature of re-structuring. It is difficult to come to any conclusion on this question, since hypnoanalysis has not yet anything like a strictly systematized technique which has proved its effectiveness and can be applied selectively to the treatment of certain nosological categories.

In certain cases of phobia, when depth therapy is impossible, temporary results may be obtained by hypnosis. If the neurosis becomes more severe and necessitates giving up work, hypnosis may have a sedative effect and enable the patient to resume work. The patient should then be oriented towards depth therapy. It would be especially interesting to study the transition from one form of therapy to the other, with the question of transference which this involves.

Obsessional neurosis. This also calls for an analytic type of treatment. We have sometimes used hypnotherapy in the case of old subjects with a significant psychasthenic background tinged with mild anxiety, whose social adjustment was normal. Previous attempts at depth therapy had not given definite results. Hypnotherapeutic treatment, combined with a supportive attitude, was successful in alleviating their symptoms. Soviet authors report positive results in the treatment of obsessional neuroses; but it seems to us that there is sometimes confusion over terminology. Certain cases seem to us rather to be cases of phobia (132, p. 92), since the symptomatology does not include obsessive rituals or propitiatory actions.

Severe neuroses or borderline cases. This type of case, at present very widespread, should not be treated by hypnosis, which would be liable to facilitate transition to psychosis. Some authors, however, have attempted to apply hypnosis in some of these cases.

Psychosis. Hypnosis is not generally used in these cases. It is generally considered that psychotics are only exceptionally hypnotizable. Moreover, it has been claimed that attempts to hypnotize schizophrenics with delusions, may make their delusions worse. It seems, however, that the problem of hypnotherapy for psychotics has developed somewhat in the past twenty years. The report of the American Psychiatric Association (183) mentions the use of hypnosis in the treatment of carefully selected psychotic cases. In the U.S.S.R., Lebedinski (132, p. 245) considers that hypnosis may be attempted in certain schizophrenics. Even the existence of delusions in these patients is not always for him a contraindication to the use of hypnosis. Some studies dealing with the hypnotherapy of schizophrenics have been published (29, 237). An American author has recently published a study (100) on the use of group hypnosis together with chlorpromazine in the treatment of chronic schizophrenics. Improvement was more rapid in the group of patients treated by both drug and hypnosis than in those who were given drug treatment only.

Very much the same thing can be said of the analytic treatment of schizophrenics as of the hypnotic treatment. These patients, whom Freud called cases of "narcissistic neurosis", were regarded as incapable of establishing a transference and therefore were not amenable to the action of this primordial psychotherapeutic lever. Then it was noticed that they did give evidence of transference, though in a modified form. It was at this point that analytic psychotherapy for psychotics was introduced. Psychotics, being capable of transference, also came to be acknowledged as hypnotizable and hypnotherapy in its turn was tried with them.

It may be wondered whether, in this development, counter-transference attitudes, like the changes which have occurred in the social environment, may not have played a big part. Therapists have become more readily available and patients are more ready to react. Since our experience of hypnotherapy with psychotics is quite limited, we are not in a position to express any definite opinion about the experience of hypnotherapists in relation to these patients, nor about the hypnotizability of the patients nor the effectiveness of the treatment.

Hypnosis may be tried in reactive or neurotic depressions. Results have been obtained with mild manic-depressives in the depressive phase, though not without relapses.

Auguste Voisin (52, pp. 147–54), in particular, last century supported the use of hypnosis in the treatment of psychoses. It is difficult to know precisely what disorders the patients hypnotized by Voisin suffered from. The word "psychosis" did not have the same meaning as it has today, and people talked of "hysterical psychosis" or "hysterical mania". Voisin declared that he could hypnotize 10 per cent of the "insane" who found their way into his department. He would sometimes spend hours and make up to twenty attempts before succeeding in putting them to sleep. Among the patients hypnotized he included a certain number with "delusions" and "hallucinations", but in general the cases calmed by hypnosis were cases showing agitation, and it is likely that the "delusions" and the "hallucinations" were of a hysterical nature, or at best symptoms of a manic-depressive psychosis and not of schizophrenia in the sense in which the term is used today. The contribution of Forel (52, p. 155) to the discussion which followed Voisin's paper at the Congress in 1889 also took this view. He had succeeded in stopping "fits of hysterical mania" but had "never succeeded in changing the course of mental diseases by suggestion." "Delusions have never been modified in any patient; even those whom I was able to hypnotize, to reduce to a state of anaesthesia or amnesia, whom I got to carry out post-hypnotic suggestions, refused to accept any suggestion at variance with their delusions." However, a "case of chronic mania with hallucinations (on the way to a systematized dementia)* showing violent attacks of rage, could be put to sleep during the attack, which was thus stopped. But the following day, the patient woke up just as bad as before."

An English author, Robertson (189), following Voisin's example, also tried hypnosis with "psychotics". He appears to have obtained a sedative effect in cases of genuine mania. It would appear, according to Robertson, "that at a certain stage of simple mania, attention is easily aroused, and the imagination is brilliant, so that the suggested sensations of sleep are vividly felt, and the hypnotic state is thus readily produced" (189, p. 3).

On the whole, our view is that great caution is required in evaluating the results of hypnotherapy with psychotics. Faulty diagnosis and the possibility of spontaneous remissions make the assessment of results especially difficult. We have seen a woman who was a genuine case of manic-depressive disorder with important neurotic elements, in whom a depression was spectacularly arrested by a few hypnotic sessions. We did not follow this patient up, but it does not seem likely that her manic-depressive illness was cured. In any case, the use of hypnosis in subjects liable to commit suicide is a delicate matter, especially in France, since the prejudice against hypnosis is liable to affect the assessment of the therapist's responsibility.

Addictions. Positive results have been reported in the treatment of chronic alcoholism and excessive smoking. In the case of smoking, the absence of follow-up studies prevents us from estimating the permanence of these results. It may well be felt that alcoholics, who are generally quite easy to hypnotize, are likely to benefit from hypnotherapy used as an addition to other therapeutic measures.

There were several papers on the hypnotherapeutic treatment of alcoholism read at the 1900 Congress (Lloyd Tuckey, 53, p. 169; De Jong, p. 178, etc.) The most important was that of the Russian Tokarsky (p. 173), which was based on 700 cases, with 80 per cent cures. Patients were considered cured if they had not started drinking again at least a year after the treatment had ended.

---

*What would be called "schizomania" in Claude's terms.

At the present time, hypnotherapy is still largely used in the treatment of alcoholism in the U.S.S.R. Konstoroum (119, p. 60) even regards alcoholism as constituting an "unconditional" indication for the use of hypnotic therapy.

Morphine addiction, again, seems to have been more amenable to hypnotherapy at the end of last century, to judge by the papers given at the 1900 Congress. At that time, a Swedish author (233) treated morphine addicts by prolonged hypnotic sessions (virtually prolonged sleep therapy). But hypnotherapy today does not seem to be of much use in drug addiction. Schilder and Kauders (197) indicate that drug addicts are especially easy to hypnotize during the weaning stage, but add that, in their experience, they always relapse in spite of that.

(c) Miscellaneous

Anaesthesiology. The effect of hypnosis on pain, allowing for example a surgical operation with laparotomy, the removal of a breast, or a thyroidectomy, constitutes an exceptional objective demonstration of the reality of hypnosis. Since the progress of chemical anaesthesia, it is true that such operations have only experimental rather than practical value. But hypnosis can also be of use in reducing pre-operative anxiety and in alleviating post-operative symptoms. Post-operative urinary retention may be relieved by suggestion; and hypnosis may also be used to obtain the first post-operative bowel movement (131).

Traumatology. Here we have yet another field of application for hypnosis. Hypnosis may be used to facilitate the accurate diagnosis of the consequences of accidents at work and later to treat the post-traumatic neuroses to which they sometimes lead. (Cases 8 and 9).

One interesting application is in the case of serious burns (57). Analgesia produced by suggestion enables the patient's suffering to be reduced and the wounds to be opened when the dressing is changed. Further, we may be able to increase the appetite so as to raise the caloric intake, a vital factor for recovery.

Case 8.

Mr. Bou . . . , 27 years of age, a North African labourer, fell on his wrist on 23rd September 1954. He was very accident-prone. A plaster immobilization was used for fracture of the scaphoid and os magnum. Two months later the plaster was removed and stiffening of the wrist with permanent flexion of the fingers was found. The patient was then given an intensive course of physical treatment. No improvement was apparent. On 1st May 1955, he was awarded a 70 per cent pension, on medical advice. Two months later, he was given up by the orthopaedist, who considered that the stiffening of the wrist and hand was equivalent to amputation. He was referred for vocational re-training, when psychiatric factors were suspected and he was sent to us for more thorough investigation. The patient was seen at Villjuif on 24th October 1955. As he was very unsophisticated, it was decided to give direct and indirect suggestions of sleep (three placebo pills were taken). Under the influence of this procedure, he appeared like a subject in a hypnotic state. But suggestions remained without effect. He started when he was touched on the hand, although in the normal waking state he did not respond in this way. Confronted with this atypical hypnotic state, we suspected a refusal to communicate as a form of defensive behaviour. The hyperaesthesia also seemed to point in this direction. We suspected a hysterical symptom in a weak personality already invalided and pensioned. The session actually had considerable emotional repercussions. The patient suffered from continual diarrhoea for the next two days, and simply could not eat. We suspected regression on the vegetative level in the face of our action, which was felt as a threat. At the next session, he was given two placebo pills without any suggestion. Left alone, he drowsed. It was then suggested to him that his digestive troubles would clear up. Three days later he was seen again. His appetite had returned and his digestive troubles had disappeared. The hysterical syndrome was confirmed. It was to receive further support from the opening of the hand under pentothal, although the patient closed it again immediately, his vigilance restored. He proved to be incurable.

We have here a case in which hypnosis was without any therapeutic effect. We are even inclined to think that the patient was not properly hypnotized. One might argue about his state of consciousness after the suggestions. It is nevertheless true that the technique of hypnosis provided a guide for diagnosis. Psychotherapy applied earlier might perhaps have been more effective.

Case 9.

Mr. Vi..., 21 years of age, was the victim of an accident on 2nd November 1955. He fell backwards while tightening a nut which gave way. He was picked up with intense pain in the back and taken to the infirmary, where the diagnosis of traumatic lumbago was made. After a fortnight in bed, he got up and was alarmed to find that he got tingling sensations in the calves and thigh and had difficulty in walking. At the beginning of December, he went into hospital at Saint-Cloud for prolapsed intervertebral disc. He was proposed for a re-training centre and was admitted, but the diagnosis was proved wrong by neurological and radiological examinations. The patient was sent home. This set off a new series of reactions – depression, moroseness, anxiety and functional impotence to such an extent that he was completely "paralysed" for a whole day. His general condition deteriorated. In this state he came to the Centre de Médecine Psychosomatique on 6th February 1956, walking with a stick.

We knew that this patient had been treated as a malingerer by some doctors. We laid emphasis rather on his ordeal. We then learned of the existence of family conflicts, especially with his father. The patient was very co-operative, and accordingly two hypnotic sessions were used, with excellent results with regard to the mobility, anxiety and moroseness. It must be added, however, that resumption of work was delayed by a feverish sore throat and temporary enuresis. This illness provided compelling grounds for return to the paternal home. The feverishness quickly disappeared and work was then resumed without difficulty.

In this case, the application of hypnosis after only a fairly short delay avoided the procession from one hospital to another, enabled the case to be diagnosed correctly and guided the treatment which succeeded in controlling the acute episode. It enabled the injured man to resume work, but was without marked influence on the neurotic personality structure, which would have needed long-term treatment. The suppression of the acute episode and the return to work may have made possible the development of other interests. One might argue here about the appearance of susbstitute symptoms (enuresis) but these were, in any case, only temporary. The patient was seen again in November 1962. He was married and the father of a child. He was well adjusted professionally, and was working with his father-in-law. His emotional equilibrium was still precarious. He had depressions and suffered from insomnia.

Oncology. Hypnosis has been used to reduce pain in terminal cancers. It may also be used to lessen the psychosomatic overlay of certain symptoms (Case 10).

Case 10.

The most dramatic case and the one which best illustrates the power of sugges-tion is that of Mr. Va . . . , a workman of 53 years of age. When we saw him, he was practically dying. He had had an operation for cancer six months previously and was now in hospital at the Institut Gustave-Roussy with dysphagia. He was extremely emaciated. His dysphagia, which allowed him only a minimum of nourishment, had no basis in any mechanical blockage. It was selective for certain foods and bore no relation to the volume or consistency of the foods in question. The dietician requested us to see him (April 1954).

There was no time for delay. Hypnosis was tried and a deep trance obtained. Suggestions were given, without result after the first session. The following day, we had another session. The patient still could not eat. The next day, we were informed that on the evening following the second session, the patient had asked for food and eaten it all. His appetite improved. In a few days, he put on two pounds in weight and his morale was transformed. He insisted on leaving hospital. He returned a fortnight later and died. An autopsy indicated no organic basis for the dysphagia.

Here we have a case where the use of hypnosis was by way of meeting an emergency and where removal of symptoms was in no way contraindicated. Hypnosis could be applied wholeheartedly and without reserve, which may have rendered the suggestions more effective. The patient was invigorated by his psychological treatment but died some days later from the inevitable fatal organic process.

PART TWO

TECHNIQUES OF HYPNOSIS

Introduction

THE technique of hypnosis depends upon the use of a certain number of "objective" (physical) procedures, the effectiveness of which is in most cases closely connected with subjective factors.

By objective procedures, we mean actions on the sensory-motor level, in particular, the reduction of sensory input and of motor expression, the fixation of attention and the repetition of monotonous stimuli. The subjective factors refer to the inter-personal level, to the relationship established between the subject and the practitioner. We have already raised the question of the practitioner's personality. We must now consider how far the practitioner can modify his attitude toward the subject. At the deep level of "being", such modification is practically impossible. But more superficially, at the level of "appearing", the attitude of the practitioner may to a certain extent be varied and be more or less authoritarian or liberal, more or less paternal or maternal, while still remaining equally benevolent.

Brenman and Gill (34) propose the following four from the range of possible attitudes; (a) an attitude of unquestionable authority, in which the practitioner simply does not doubt the efficacy of the suggestions, (b) an intellectual approach, in which he explains all that he does, (c) an emotional approach, in which he can use the patient's need for sympathy, comfort and security, and finally (d) a passive approach, in which he says that he can do nothing without the patient, who is thus given the impression that he does it all himself.

Precise rules about attitudes cannot be laid down. The practitioner will naturally be helped by the knowledge of the patient's personality which he will have acquired during the *anamnestic session*. But above all, intuition will play the most important part. It goes without saying that, in addition, the physician's attitude will be influenced by the patient's personality, which will provoke counter-transference reactions in him. In all cases, an

95

atmosphere of confidence must be created. This will emerge in the first instance from communication at the non-verbal level, but it may be reinforced verbally in the preparatory talk. This preparatory talk will take place after the anamnestic session, during which a diagnosis will have been made and the advisability of hypnotic therapy considered.

The Preparatory Talk

THE content of this talk will naturally be determined by the subject's socio-cultural level. He should be asked what he knows of hypnosis. It is convenient at this point to remove any apprehensions, prejudices or false ideas which he may have acquired. Thus, if he has attended hypnotic sessions conducted by a stage hypnotist,* it may be explained to him that the treatment which he is to receive has nothing in common with what he saw on the stage; that he need not fear that he will be made ridiculous, nor that he will be transformed into a robot; that his will will be left intact; that if he resists being hypnotized, he will not feel any effects from it, but even if he is amenable to it, he will have an active part throughout. He ought then to co-operate to at least some extent with the physician. The physician will tell him what hypnosis consists of. It is very difficult to give a precise description, since the experience of hypnosis varies from one subject to another. The physician may use analogies. Thus, he may explain that the hypnotic state is an intermediate state between wakefulness and sleep, through which we normally pass every night before going to sleep, and which lasts only a very short time then, but can profitably be made longer now. He may say that hypnosis is like a state in which we dream and know that we are dreaming; and that during this state, the patient will remain in communication with the physician. This kind of selective communication may be illustrated by the example of the mother who, although she is asleep and is insensible to any other sound, yet hears her child's slightest cry. It may be added that

---

*We ourselves attempted induction by the method of simple direct suggestion with a woman patient with whom we had not raised the question of prior knowledge. She was completely refractory. She explained that she did not think that she was being hypnotized, since what she had seen on the stage was very different; there, the hypnotist fascinated the subject and the latter gave in completely and was wholly under the hypnotist's control. After an explanatory talk (which almost certainly had both rational and non-rational effects), the patient became more amenable to hypnosis.

everyone is to some extent hypnotizable; and that some subjects feel only a mild sleepiness, while others rapidly find themselves quite unable to move.

Hypnosis, it may be explained, is a continuum stretching from mere relaxation to somnambulism, which generally includes complete post-hypnotic amnesia and sometimes the ability to experience hallucinations as a result of suggestion. Amnesia need not inevitably occur; if the subject is very anxious to remember what has happened during the hypnotic session, he may be able to do so.

It will be found that among the subjects who come to the physician, there are some who are attracted by the "magic" aspect of hypnosis and who really prefer not to be given any explanation. The physician naturally does not like this, since he sees his procedures losing their scientific character and becoming like those of a quack. If, however, the patient's image of the therapist is beneficial to him, perhaps the therapist should not be too ready to destroy this image by insisting upon a more rational interpretation. This kind of role may in fact create emotional problems for the therapist and limit his effectiveness in certain cases. The following example well illustrates this kind of problem. We had to hypnotize a female patient of 55 years of age who had already been successfully treated by a London therapist (the patient was in fact the manic-depressive referred to on p. 89). She was a woman of considerable culture and we had chosen an intellectual approach with a great deal of explanation. The patient was disappointed. She told us in all seriousness that her English therapist made her think of an "Irish witch-doctor", and that she found this to be necessary. With our method, she could no longer believe in witchcraft and broke off treatment. Two years later we met the therapist in London and asked him whether he knew anything about the patient. He told us that she had come to see him again, but that he had got rid of her because he did not want to continue treating her. Although he did not accept psycho-analytic explanations of hypnosis, he gave as his reason the "excessively violent transference" which the patient had developed in relation to himself.

Tests of Suggestibility

TESTS of suggestibility are given after the preparatory talk and before induction proper begins. The relations between suggestibility and hypnotizability are controversial. Suggestible subjects have not been proved to be more easily hypnotized than others, nor vice versa. The tests in question do, however, serve to give the patient confidence in his ability to receive suggestions. We shall describe three which are in current use, Kohnstamm's procedure (rather than test), the body-sway test and the hand-clasp test.

In *Kohnstamm's procedure,* the patient is asked to stand with one side against a wall and to press against the wall with the back of his bent wrist as hard as he can. He has to keep his eyes shut. For about a minute, the physician gives the patient instructions such as,

"Press very hard, stiffen the muscles of your shoulder and arm."

After this, he asks the patient to walk away from the wall with his arms hanging loosely by his sides. Most frequently, the arm which has been used will rise of its own accord, sometimes through an angle of 90 degrees. It is explained to the patient that the relaxation which he has experienced and the involuntary movement of his arm resemble the relaxation and surrender to outside forces which he will have to try to achieve again during hypnotic induction.

In the *body-sway test,* the patient stands with his feet together, his body perfectly erect and his eyes fixed on a point on the ceiling just above his head. The physician, who stands behind the patient, asks him to shut his eyes but to remain standing. Then he tells the patient,

"I am going to measure your capacity for relaxation. I am putting my hands on your shoulders."

The physician, having done this, then adds,

"Now I am going to press my hands on your shoulders and you will feel a force pulling you back against me. Do not resist it. I will hold you up when you fall."

You are falling, you are falling, you are falling, you are being pulled back ... You are falling, you are falling."

At this point, the physician removes his hands and the patient begins to oscillate gently. If he fails to do so, the physician puts his hands back on the patient's shoulders and makes him sway backwards and forwards, telling him that he is resisting and asking him to let himself go. He gives further suggestions of falling backwards and suddenly removes his hands. When the patient begins to oscillate, the suggestions become stronger.

"You are falling backwards, you are falling, you are falling, you are falling backwards, backwards, I will hold you when you fall."

The physician must naturally be in a position to hold the patient up.

If we have to work with a group, the *hand-clasp test* has the advantage that it can be given to several people at once. The physician asks the patient, who is seated on a chair, to clasp his hands tightly together. He shows the patient what to do, and says,

"I want you to close your eyes for a moment and think of a heavy metal vice, the jaws of which tighten on a screw. Imagine that your hands are like the jaws of the vice. I am going to count up to five. As I count, your hands will clasp tighter and tighter, tighter and tighter, tighter and tighter. When I get to five, your hands will be so tightly clasped that it will be difficult or impossible for you to separate them. One, clasp; two, clasp tighter, tighter, tighter; three, clasp very tightly, your hands are fixed together; four, your hands are very firmly locked together, very firmly locked; five, they are so tightly locked that even if you try to separate them, they will remain locked together until I tell you to unclasp them. Now, unclasp them slowly."

We have given ready made formulae, and we shall later have occasion to give many more. We hope that they will be of assistance to beginners. But they are only illustrations and may be varied to any desired extent.

Induction

BEFORE we describe the technique of induction, we must give some idea of the stages of hypnosis. Between the normal waking state and a deep trance there is a whole range of intermediate states. Liébeault distinguished ten, Bernheim nine. At the present time, we speak of light, medium and deep hypnosis. To measure hypnotizability, scales have been devised but their value is necessarily relative because of the lability and subjectivity of the phenomena. The most widely used is that of Davis and Husband, which has thirty categories (Table 1).

The first problem in induction is to know whether the patient should lie down or sit in an armchair. There is no fixed rule. Some practitioners use only one or the other position, while others use both. Most patients say that they are indifferent. Experience, however, shows that some anxious subjects do better in an armchair. Some patients prefer to lie down, and some physicians think that this position is the most favourable, in so far as it facilitates relaxation and approaches the position adopted in sleep. Whatever position is taken, it is essential to see that the patient is perfectly comfortable. He should be told to assume a completely passive attitude and to let himself go without making any effort or offering any resistance. He must not ask any questions about what is going to happen to him, but simply accept it.

When these preliminaries have been seen to, we come to induction proper. Before describing the methods in current use, we shall go back to the technique employed by Bernheim in 1884, as described in his own words.

" 'Look at me and think of nothing but sleep. Your eyelids begin to feel heavy, your eyes are tired. They begin to wink, they are getting moist, you cannot see distinctly. They are closed.' Some patients close their eyes and are asleep immediately. With others, I have to repeat, lay more stress on what I say, and even make gestures. It makes little difference what sort of gesture is made. I hold two fingers of my right hand before the patient's eyes and ask him to look at them, or pass both hands several times before his eyes, or persuade him to fix his eyes upon mine, endeavouring, at the same time, to concentrate his attention on the idea of sleep. I say, 'Your lids are closing, you cannot open them again. Your arms feel heavy, so do your legs. You cannot feel anything. Your hands are motionless. You see nothing, you are going to sleep.' And I add in a commanding tone, 'Sleep.' This word often turns the balance. The eyes close and the patient sleeps or is at least influenced . . .

TABLE 1

HYPNOTIC SUSCEPTIBILITY SCORING SYSTEM

Depth	Score	Objective symptoms
Insusceptible	0	
Light trance	1	
	2	Relaxation
	3	Fluttering of lids
	4	Closing of eyes
	5	Complete physical relaxation
	6	Catalepsy of eyes
	7	Limb catalepsies
	10	Rigid catalepsy
	11	Anaesthesia (glove)
Medium trance	13	Partial amnesia
	15	Post-hypnotic anaesthesia
	17	Personality changes
	18	Simple post-hypnotic suggestions
	20	Kinaesthetic delusions; complete amnesia
Somnambulistic trance	21	Ability to open eyes without affecting trance
	23	Bizarre post-hypnotic suggestions
	25	Complete somnambulism
	26	Positive visual hallucinations
	27	Positive auditory hallucinations, post-hypnotic
	28	Systematized post-hypnotic amnesias
	29	Negative auditory hallucinations
	30	Negative visual hallucinations; hyperaesthesias

"If the patient does not shut his eyes or keep them shut, I do not require them to be fixed on mine, or on my fingers, for any length of time, for it sometimes happens that they remain wide open indefinitely, and instead of the idea of sleep being conceived, only a rigid fixation of the eyes results. In this case, closure of the eyes by the operator succeeds better. After keeping them fixed one or two minutes, I push the eyelids down, or stretch them slowly over the eyes, gradually closing them more and more and so imitating the process of natural sleep. Finally,

I keep them closed, repeating the suggestion, 'Your lids are stuck together; you cannot open them. The need of sleep becomes greater and greater, you can no longer resist.' I lower my voice gradually, repeating the command, 'Sleep', and it is very seldom that more than three minutes pass before sleep or some degree of hypnotic influence is obtained. It is sleep by suggestion—a type of sleep which I insinuate into the brain . . .

"I sometimes succeed by keeping the eyes closed for some time, commanding silence and quiet, talking continuously, and repeating the same formulas. 'You feel a sort of drowsiness, a torpor; your arms and legs are motionless. Your eyelids are warm. Your nervous system is quiet; you have no will. Your eyes remain closed. Sleep is coming, etc.' After keeping up this auditory suggestion for several minutes, I remove my fingers. The eyes remain closed. I raise the patient's arms; they remain uplifted. We have induced cataleptic sleep . . .

"Whilst with some patients success is more readily obtained by acting quietly, with others quiet suggestion has no effect. With these, it is better to be abrupt, to restrain with an authoritative voice the inclination to laugh, or the weak and involuntary resistance which this manoeuvre may provoke" (20, pp. 1–4).

We shall now describe the methods used by modern practitioners, starting with the most widely used.

Hypnosis by fixation of an object. The practitioner gets the patient to fixate an object—a pencil, a key, a coin, a coloured ball suspended on a piece of string, or perhaps a point on the ceiling or wall, or on the physician's desk. The object should be about one foot from the patient's eyes. If a point is fixated, it may be further away.

The practitioner then gives a series of suggestions for a period which may be longer or shorter according to the subject's responsiveness. These suggestions, like all those to follow, are given in a monotonous voice, are repeated many times over and are always of a concrete and vivid nature.

The practitioner suggests in turn a feeling of general relaxation, of drowsiness, of heaviness, of warmth and finally of sleep. These suggestions may be given in the following form, but may naturally be varied in many ways.

"I am holding an object in front of you. You are looking at this object. You are listening to my voice. If your eyes wander, bring them back to the object and keep looking at it. Relax and listen to my voice. I want you to relax. You feel relaxed all over. You are feeling more and more relaxed. While you look at the object and listen to my voice, you feel more and more relaxed. The muscles of your feet are relaxed, your whole body is relaxed. You also feel sleepy. You are going to feel sleepier and sleepier. Listen carefully to my voice. Now a feeling of heaviness is creeping over you, your body is becoming heavy. Your feet and your legs and your whole body are becoming heavy, heavy, heavy. A pleasant warmth suffuses your body. You are thinking of sleep. A pleasant warmth suffuses you just as when you fall asleep. Your eyelids are getting heavy, you are getting sleepy, your eyelids are getting heavy, heavy, heavy. Think about sleep and nothing else. You can no longer keep your eyes open, your eyelids are getting heavier and heavier. You feel sleepy, more and more sleepy, you are getting tired of looking, your eyes are smarting, they are watering (this should be said when the eyes are observed to be getting moist). Breathe deeply, very deeply and slowly. At every breath your sleep is getting deeper, your eyes are now shut. You are going to sleep, sleep, sleep."

Generally, the repetition of these suggestions gets the patient's eyes to close. The physician may, to end with, lay his fingers on the subject's closed eyes. If the subject has not spontaneously closed his eyes, recourse may be had to a counting technique. This consists of repeating the suggestions, counting from one to ten for the different stages. If, after this, the subject still does not close his eyes, the practitioner may, following Bernheim, use the following procedure. He puts his hand an inch or two from the patient's eyes and moves it up and down, alternately, many times over. At the same time, for about two minutes, he repeats,

"Follow my hand, up, down, up, down, and you will feel sleepy, sleepier and sleepier."

If the patient still keeps his eyes open, the practitioner may say to him,

"Now, you can close your eyes,"

and at this point gently close the patient's eyelids with his fingers. Another procedure consists of placing the first and second fingers in front of the patient's eyes and saying to him,

"Your eyes are getting heavy and you feel like going to sleep. Watch my fingers carefully. I am going to bring them nearer and nearer your eyes, and your eyes will close."

The patient naturally cannot help closing his eyes when the practitioner's fingers are very near and, at that moment, the practitioner presses against the eyelids. He tells the patient that his eyelids will remain closed until he is told to open them again.

If we compare the method which we have just described with that used by Bernheim, we find that the principles have remained unchanged through eighty years, although there are some minor differences in their application. There seems to be less recourse nowadays to the authoritarian attitude recommended by Bernheim. Again, with Bernheim the stage of induction does not appear to have lasted more than ten minutes. Today, this is considered insufficient. Brenman and Gill (34) consider that several sessions of from fifty minutes to an hour and a half each are necessary to induce deep hypnosis in a neurotic person. Erickson (67) even goes so far as to say that, in some cases, success is achieved after several sessions of up to three or four hours, during which any semblance of routine must be avoided.

We now come to the method of *pure verbal suggestion* (without fixation of any object). It is used especially when the patient has difficulty in fixating visually. In this method, the patient lies stretched out on a couch and is asked to close his eyes. Suggestions are then given somewhat as follows.

"I want you to relax, to relax your whole body. I want you to feel all the tension in your muscles, in all your muscles, and then to relax. Relax your forehead, relax the muscles of your face. Relax. Relax your neck muscles, your arm muscles, your leg muscles, the muscles of your whole body. Stretch your arms and legs. You feel a sluggishness and lassitude all over your body. Now you feel the pressure of the pillow against your head. You feel the pressure of the pillow against your neck and shoulders. You feel the couch along your back. Now you concentrate on your thighs and you can feel the couch holding you up. You are very, very relaxed. It feels as if your body were sinking into the couch, sinking right into it. I want you to think of a nice, pleasant place where you can stretch out and forget all your cares and worries, a place where you can go to sleep. It might be at the seaside, or in the hills or any other place you like (the patient most frequently chooses the hills). You are breathing slowly and deeply. Stretch your legs and arms. Your body is limp and relaxed (the practitioner lifts the patient's arm and lets it fall again). You are very relaxed, very, very relaxed. Your whole body is relaxed. You are stretched out somewhere in the hills. It is a very still day. The sky is blue and the sun is bright. You are looking at the sky. You see a light cloud. Everything is calm and peaceful. Your mind is also perfectly at peace. You smell the scent of the pines and you can see the water of a lake. Your mind becomes as tranquil as the surface of the lake. Relax and sleep, sleep, sleep, sleep peacefully and deeply, sleep."

Induction may stop at this point. Wolberg prolongs the technique and adds the following suggestions.

"As you start getting sleepy, your arm, your right arm will get light, like a feather. It will get lighter and lighter, and then it will lift—up—up—up. The sleepier you get, the lighter your arm will feel, and the higher it will lift until it touches your face. As you relax, your hand and arm lift and rise higher and higher, and when your hand touches your face, you will be asleep, deeply asleep. Your arm is rising slowly now, just like a feather—up—up—up—higher and higher and higher. It is getting close to your face, you will be asleep, deeply asleep. Now your hand has touched your face and you are asleep" (236, p. 125).

The next method to be considered is *hypnosis by fascination or eye-gaze*. It is seldom used at the present time. There are two forms of this method. It is used by some German and Russian authors in the same way as the object-fixation method, except that in this case, the patient is asked to look into the physician's eyes instead of fixating some object. It does not have to be particularly authoritarian. This is not true of its second form, in which "fascination" and authoritarianism are of the first importance. This is the method which is usually employed by stage-hypnotists. It is occasionally used in medicine, in some cases of alcoholism and addiction, and with some psychopathic personalities (Wolberg, 236).

To practise the eye-gaze method in this latter form, the physician must face the patient, about fifteen inches away. He must look down on the patient, and if the latter is taller than the practitioner the practitioner must make the patient sit down while he himself remains standing. Then he takes the patient by the shoulders and rocks him slowly backwards and forwards, with his gaze fixed upon the bridge of the patient's nose. He then gives the following series of suggestions.

"Look into my eyes. Your eyes are getting heavy, heavy, your arms are getting heavy, your legs are getting heavy, your whole body is getting heavy. Your eyes are tired, but do not close them until you feel that you cannot keep them open any longer. Your eyelids are as heavy as lead. You are going to sleep, to sleep."

The practitioner then pauses. When the patient's eyes begin to blink, he assumes a more commanding tone and says, "Your eyes are blinking, you are going to sleep, to sleep: nothing can stop you, you are going to sleep, to sleep."

As soon as the patient's eyes close, the practitioner places his hand upon them and says to the patient,

"Your eyelids are stuck together; you cannot open them until I tell you to."

The patient must then be made to sit down in an armchair.

This kind of method requires the practitioner to practise in order to get used to staring without blinking his eyes. For a few minutes every day he should stare at some object about fifteen inches away from him. He must also be sure that his eyes will not water. Another risk is that during the procedure the hypnotist himself may become hypnotized (see the self-report by E. Speer, 209).

The next method is the *hand-levitation method* developed by Erickson in 1923,* the best description of which is to be found in Wolberg (236). It is used especially by American authors. Its application is more difficult and requires long practice. For those who have mastered it, it has the great advantage that it gets the patient to participate in the induction and prepares the way for the possible use later of non-directive or analytical psychotherapy. We give it in full, quoting from Wolberg (236), who reports verbatim a recorded session.

" 'I want you to sit comfortably in your chair and relax. As you sit there, bring both hands palms down on your thighs—just like that. Keep watching your hands, and you will notice that you are able to observe them closely.

---

*Personal communication.

" 'What you will do now is sit in the chair and relax. Then you will notice that certain things happen in the course of relaxing. They have always happened while relaxing, but you have not noticed them so closely before. I am going to point them out to you. I'd like to have you concentrate on all sensations and feelings in your hands no matter what they may be . . . Perhaps you may feel the heaviness of your hand as it lies on your thigh, or you may feel pressure. Perhaps you will feel the texture of your trousers as they press against the palm of your hand; or the warmth of your hand on your thigh. Perhaps you may feel tingling. No matter what sensations there are, I want you to observe them. Keep watching your hand, and you will notice how still it is, how it remains in one position. There is motion there, but it is not yet noticeable. I want you to keep watching your hand. Your attention may wander from the hand, but it will always return back to the hand, and you keep watching the hand and wondering when the motion that is there will show itself.'

"(At this point the patient's attention is fixed on his hand. He is curious about what will happen, and sensations such as any person might experience are suggested to him as possibilities. No attempt is being made to force any suggestions on him, and if he observes any sensations or feelings, he incorporates them as a product of his own experience. The object eventually is to get him to respond to the suggestions of the hypnotist as if these too are parts of his own experience. A subtle attempt is being made to get him to associate his sensations with the words spoken to him so that words or commands uttered by the hypnotist will evoke sensory or motor responses later on. Unless the patient is consciously resisting, a slight motion or jerking will develop in one of the fingers or in the hand. As soon as this happens, the hypnotist mentions it and remarks that the motion will probably increase. The hypnotist must also comment on any other observable reaction of the patient, such as the motion of the legs or deep breathing. The result of this linking of the patient's reactions with comments of the hypnotist is an association of the two in the patient's mind.)

" 'It will be interesting to see which one of the fingers will move first. It may be the middle finger, or the forefinger, or the ring finger, or the little finger, or the thumb. One of the fingers is going to jerk or move. You don't know exactly when or in which hand. Keep watching and you will begin to notice a slight movement, possibly in the right hand. There, the thumb jerks and moves, just like that.

" 'As the movement begins, you will notice an interesting thing. Very slowly the space between the fingers will widen, the fingers will slowly move apart, and you'll notice that the spaces will get wider and wider and wider. They'll move apart slowly; the fingers will seem to be spreading apart, wider and wider and wider. The fingers are spreading, wider and wider and wider apart, just like that.'

"(This is the first real suggestion to which the patient is expected to respond. If the fingers start spreading apart, they do so because the patient is reacting to suggestion. The hypnotist continues to talk as if the response is one that would have come about by itself in the natural course of events.)

" 'As the fingers spread apart, you will notice that the fingers will soon want to arch up from the thigh, as if they want to lift, higher and higher. (*The patient's index finger starts moving upward slightly.*) Notice how the index finger lifts. As it does the other fingers want to follow—up, up, slowly rising. (*The other fingers start lifting.*)

" 'As the fingers lift you'll become aware of lightness in the hand, a feeling of lightness, so much so that the fingers will arch up, and the whole hand will slowly lift and rise as if it feels like a feather, as if a balloon is lifting it up in the air, lifting —up—up—up, pulling up higher and higher and higher, the hand becoming very light. (*The hand starts rising.*) As you watch your hand rise, you'll notice that the arm comes up, up, up in the air, a little higher—and higher—and higher—and higher, up—up—up. (*The arm has lifted about five inches above the thigh and the patient is gazing at it fixedly.*)

" 'Keep watching the hand and arm as it rises straight up, and as it does you will soon become aware of how drowsy and tired your eyes become. As your arm continues to rise, you will get tired and relaxed and sleepy, very sleepy. Your eyes will get heavy and your lids may want to close. And as your arm rises higher and higher, you will want to enjoy the peaceful, relaxed feeling of letting your eyes close and of being sleepy.'

"(It will be noticed that as the patient executes one suggestion, his positive response is used to reinforce the next suggestion. For instance, as his arm rises, it is suggested in essence that he will get drowsy because his arm is rising.)

" 'Your arm lifts—up—up—and you are getting very drowsy; your lids get very heavy, your breathing gets slow and regular. Breathe deeply—in and out. (*The patient holds his arm stretched out directly in front of him, his eyes are blinking and his breathing is deep and regular.*) As you keep watching your hand and arm and feeling more and more drowsy and relaxed, you will notice that the direction of the hand will change. The arm will bend and the hand will move closer and closer to your face—up—up—up—and as it rises you will slowly but steadily go into a deep, deep sleep in which you relax deeply and to your own satisfaction. The arm will continue to rise up—up—lifting, lifting—up in the air until it touches your face, and you will get sleepier and sleepier, but you must not go to sleep until your hand touches your face. When your hand touches your face, you will be asleep, deeply asleep.'

"(The patient here is requested to choose his own pace in falling asleep, so that when his hand touches his face, he feels himself to be asleep to his own satisfaction. Hand levitation and sleepiness continue to reinforce each other. When the patient finally does close his eyes, he will have entered a trance with his own co-operation. He will later be less inclined to deny that he was in a trance.)

" 'Your hand is now changing its direction. It moves up—up—up toward your face. Your eyelids are getting heavy. You are getting sleepier, and sleepier, and sleepier. (*The patient's hand is approaching his face, his eyelids are blinking more rapidly.*) Your eyes get heavy, very heavy, and the hand moves straight up towards your face. You get very tired and drowsy. Your eyes are closing, are closing. When your hand touches your face you'll be asleep, deeply asleep. You'll feel very drowsy. You feel drowsier and drowsier and drowsier, very sleepy, very tired. Your eyes are like lead, and your hand moves up, up, up, right towards your face, and when it reaches your face, you will be asleep. (*The patient's hand touches his face and his eyes close.*) Go to sleep, go to sleep, just asleep. And as you sleep you feel very tired and relaxed. I want you to concentrate on relaxation, a state of tensionless relaxation. Think of nothing else, but sleep, deep sleep.' "

In the methods which we have outlined above, verbal suggestions were used as auditory stimuli. With subjects who have an unconscious fear of the therapist, or who are unable to concentrate on words, the *metronome procedure* may be used. This is based upon the mechanical repetition of an auditory stimulus. The beat of the metronome helps the subject to concentrate. The practitioner suggests to him that he will get sleepier and sleepier as he goes on listening to the beat.

There are also other methods of hypnotizing without verbal suggestion, for example, Mesmer's passes, Braid's fixation method, Luys' mirror and so on. Ivanov-Smolenski (102) reviews these methods and adds his own method of hypnotizing with the help of luminous and thermal stimuli. The Australian author, Meares (147, 148), describes a technique of hypnotizing which depends on non-verbal communication and an appropriate setting. All verbal communication takes place during the anamnestic interview at the first session. A physical examination is also made during this session. Meares emphasizes the significance of the physical examination, which performs the double function of inducing a state of passive "submissiveness" in the patient and accustoming him to non-verbal communication by touch. Hypnosis proper takes place at the following session. Meares describes his procedure as follows (148).

"I talk very little. By my behaviour I try to communicate the idea of relaxation and calm. I aim to establish a feeling of community with the patient. I look out the window, and the patient looks out the window. The idea of calm is further communicated by unverbalized phonation, by occasional "ums" or "ahs". If the patient shows the slightest sign of anxiety I assume a flow of leisurely inconsequential conversation which does not require any reply. The patient's anxiety soon ceases. The patient is then told to slip off his clothes just as he did on his previous visit, and to pull the blanket over himself. At this stage, I wander out of the room leaving the patient to himself. When I return in a few minutes the patient is lying on the couch in his underclothes covered by a blanket. I come in leisurely, and do not say anything. If the patient shows the slightest signs of anxiety, I move closer to him. If the anxiety persists I take a plessor and leisurely elicit the tendon reflexes as on the previous visit. An unverbalized grunt of satisfaction further reassures the patient, and his anxiety passes. Then, still without saying anything, I move away from the patient. I move about a little to let him know that I am there. If there is any return of anxiety as shown by the slightest tensing of his facial expression, or by minute movement of his fingers, I move towards him. His unawareness that I have perceived his anxiety, and have immediately responded gives the patient a feeling of security, and the signs of slight anxiety usually cease. If they persist I move closer to the couch, and I communicate by pulling up the corner of the blanket, or if necessary I gently palpate the abdomen as I did during the physical examination. The patient's anxiety fades, and I again move away from him. The procedure is continued with appropriate variations."

After some minutes the subject goes into a state of deep hypnosis. This technique is still at the experimental stage. It has been successful with a sample of 20 unselected cases.

In spite of the importance of non-verbal communication, however, one should not underestimate the importance of verbal communication and wording in hypnosis. For example, we had occasion to treat a young girl of 13 years of age, who was in a urology ward for complete incontinence (stress and nocturnal) which had suddenly started. The patient had had no previous trouble with her sphincters. She was treated by suggestion. The words in which the verbal suggestions were given included the phrase "retain your urine". After the third session, the incontinence had changed into retention. This yielded to verbal suggestions more precisely expressed. It is difficult to be sure of the part played here by the wording. It is possible that retention replaced incontinence in the course of psychodynamic development in the psychotherapeutic relationship, since both symptoms refer to the same zone and belong to the same level of regression. Nevertheless, it is our impression that the wording did have a certain significance.

Deepening the Trance

By MEANS of the procedures which have been described, the subject is induced to close his eyes and to remain motionless. But he is not necessarily hypnotized, unless certain characteristic indications are present. An experienced practitioner may perhaps guess at the subject's state in some cases; but even he will often be wrong. Attempts are therefore made to induce certain hypnotic phenomena in the subject which may enable the depth of the trance to be measured. The order in which these phenomena appear is taken into consideration, according to some scale such as that of Davis and Husband (59). All scales of this kind are of course only relative. It is agreed that the procedures involved also have the effect of deepening the trance. The trance may, however, be deep right from the start, and moreover may deepen of its own accord as it continues, without any outside intervention.

It is difficult to say at what point the practitioner should test for the appearance of a phenomenon which he has been attempting to produce by a series of suggestions. As far as possible, testing should be avoided until the result is almost certain to be positive. Every practitioner must act according to his own temperament and depend upon his own ability to sense what is happening.

The first phenomenon which the practitioner attempts to produce is *heaviness of the arm*. The patient is given suggestions something like this.

"Now you are concentrating on your arm. It is getting very heavy, very, very heavy, like lead. The feeling of heaviness begins in your shoulder and comes down your arm, down your fore-arm into your hand, into your fingers, into each finger, into your thumb, your forefinger, your middle finger, your ring finger, your little finger. Your whole arm is getting as heavy as if it were holding up a 100 pound weight. I am going to count up to five, and your arm will get heavier and heavier. One, heavy. Two, very heavy. Three, even heavier, as heavy as lead. Four, even heavier yet, even heavier. Five, very, very, very heavy. You can no longer move your arm, it is so heavy."

If it is felt that the suggestion of weight has been effective, the time has come to test it. The following suggestions are given.

111

"Your arm is very, very heavy. You feel it harder and harder to move your arm. The more you try, the harder it is. Your arm is very heavy and you cannot move it. You try, but you can't."

One may also say to the patient,

"I am going to count up to five. Your arm is getting very, very heavy. When I get to 'five', you will try to lift your arm but you won't be able to. The more you try, the harder it will get to lift it."

If, after this, the patient lifts his arm, this is a sign that he is not hypnotized. The practitioner will then tell him that his case is not unique and that many people do not pass this test at the first attempt. The patient can generally be got to agree that he has felt a certain degree of heaviness and that he may well succeed at a second attempt. But if the suggestions have been successful, the patient simply cannot move his arm. Every contraction of the flexor muscles is accompanied by an opposing contraction of the extensors, of an equal or even greater strength. The arm becomes stiff and may betray the conflicting muscular contractions by a slight trembling. This tension should encourage the practitioner, who should maintain the flow of suggestions. When the signs of muscular tension are not observable, this is occasionally because the subject does not really try as hard as he can to raise his arm, out of deference to the hypnotist.

If some patients show signs of anxiety when they find that they cannot lift their arms, they should be told that the procedure is not an essential part of hypnosis, and that their arm might just as well have been made to feel extremely light.

Some authors proceed to the heaviness test in a rather different way. After giving suggestions of heaviness in the way described above, they do not ask the subject to try to lift his arm, but inform him that they are going to lift his arm and that he will not be able to prevent it from dropping again, because it is so heavy. The practitioner then lifts the patient's arm, which will generally drop back again of its own accord. If the patient is able to keep his arm up, the practitioner goes on with the suggestions, and he will rarely fail in the long run. If, however, the patient remains able to move his arm, then he is not hypnotized, and the procedure should be as we have indicated above.

Some authors go directly from the arm-heaviness test to the eyelid catalepsy test. Others introduce an intermediate *arm-rigidity test,* with test suggestions that the patient cannot bend his arm. The procedure is as follows. The practitioner stretches out the patient's arm horizontally, stroking it as he does so, and says,

"Your arm is heavy and it is getting stiff, as stiff as an iron bar. As I stroke it, it gets stiffer and stiffer. The muscles become more and more rigid. You cannot lift your arm, it is very heavy and very stiff. You cannot lift it. Try to lift it and you will find that you can't. It is as heavy as lead and as stiff as an iron bar. It gets stiffer and stiffer and you cannot bend it. The harder you try to bend it, the stiffer it gets", and so on.

After the arm-heaviness test, whether or not followed by the rigidity test, the patient is left for a few minutes. He is given suggestions of relaxation and sleep so that he may sleep for a few minutes before passing on to the next test. This is the *eyelid catelepsy test*. It is important, as with all these tests, to choose the right moment. The suggestions given are something like this.

"You are very calm and very relaxed. All your muscles are relaxed. The muscles of your head, your neck, your shoulders, your arms, your legs and your whole body are relaxed. Your breathing is deep, slow and regular. You are very, very sleepy.

You are nice and warm and comfortable. You realize that you can hear nothing except my voice. You feel your eyelids getting very, very heavy, like lead. They are stuck together and even if you try to open them they will remain closed, until I tell you to open them. They are closed, stuck together and the harder you try to open them, the tighter they remain closed, stuck together. Try to open them and you will see that you can't."

In general, the suggestions make the patient unable to open his eyes. If, however, he does open them, it should be pointed out that he has experienced some resistance to opening his eyes, and that consequently the suggestions of sleep have had some effect. He should be advised to concentrate on sleep and to try neither to keep his eyes open nor to close them voluntarily. The practitioner should then press lightly with his fingers on the patient's eyelids, and tell him that at the next session, he will fall into a state of more complete relaxation which will be like sleep.

The suggestions of sleep should be renewed before passing on to the next test. Some people who are resistant to the eyelid catalepsy test nevertheless are able to enter a good trance. Generally, we now proceed to induce *anaesthesia,* and we start by suggesting a state of *hyperaesthesia,* which is more readily obtained. The practitioner says to the patient, for example,

"Imagine that you are walking about in a very large room and you see a tank full of hot water, from which steam is rising. As soon as you see this tank, you will gently raise your right hand. Now you see it. Right. Your arm is rising. Let it fall again. Now you are approaching the tank, and you want to know how hot the water is. You plunge your right hand into the tank, and you feel it very hot. As soon as you feel this heat, you will show me by raising your hand. It goes up,

very good. Now, I am going to touch the back of your right hand with the point
of a pin, and your hand has become so sensitive that you will feel a very sharp
pain. I am then going to touch your other hand and you will see the difference.
I touch the back of your left hand and you do not feel any pain." (The hypnotized
subject will react by grimacing with pain when his right hand is touched; if he
should fail to notice any difference in the sensitivity of his two hands, he should
be told that some practice is needed in order to notice the difference, and that he
will almost certainly be able to do so at the next session. The trance is then ended.)

When the state of hyperaesthesia has been obtained, we go on
to induce *anaesthesia*. At the first session, complete anaesthesia
will not be achieved, but partial anaesthesia should be. Suggestions
such as the following should be given.

"While your right hand has got very sensitive, your left hand has lost its sensitivity. Your left hand is quite numb. If I prick it, you will not feel a real pain, as
you do in the other hand. Imagine you have a heavy leather glove on your hand.
As soon as you can see this glove, tell me by raising your hand. Your hand feels
this glove, and when I press with the pin, it will feel as if I were pressing only on
the glove (*the hand rises*). I am going to let you feel the difference when I press the
pin on the one hand and on the other (the practitioner proceeds to carry out what
he has just said he is going to do). Now your left hand is getting more and more
insensitive and numb. This insensitivity affects your whole hand, fingers and
palm. You have the feeling that your hand is encased in wood. You feel no pain.
Can you feel the numbness?"

(If the subject replies that he can still feel pain, he should be
told that this pain is very much less than that which he feels in
his other hand. It should be added that at the next session, his
left hand will be even more insensitive.)

The next hypnotic phenomenon to be considered in assessing
the depth of trance is *amnesia* (amnesia often accompanies a
deep trance, but a deep trance may sometimes occur without
amnesia). What distinguishes amnesia from the hypnotic phenomena which we have considered so far, is that its presence can
only be established when the patient wakes up. It should be
remembered that hypnotic amnesia is not a deep amnesia and
that it may be removed by the therapist. This feature has been
particularly stressed by Bernheim. Bernheim, it may be remembered, had shown Freud a hypnotized female patient whose
memory for what had happened during the hypnotic session he
had been able to revive by his insistence. It was in this way that
Freud came to think of a manipulation of memory which would
provide him with "the power of forcing the forgotten facts and
connexions into consciousness" (Freud, 81, p. 49).

The amnesia may be spontaneous or induced by post-hypnotic
suggestion. The practitioner should start by considering what the

subject may have forgotten of the trance. If it appears that he might remember everything and amnesia is thought to be desirable for psychotherapeutic purposes, the patient may be given some training to make him forget either certain aspects of the trance or the whole trance. Wolberg (236) proposes the following procedure. Immediately before the end of the next hypnotic session, the subject is told to imagine that he is asleep at home, and that he is having a dream. Shortly after, his eyes will open and he will wake up with a start. He will now have the impression of awakening from a sound sleep. He will remember his dream clearly, but will have only a vague memory of the other events in the trance. He may even have forgotten some of them completely.

If a partial amnesia has been obtained in the subject during this session, he should be told during the next session that forgetting is a normal phenomenon which may be of use in therapy. It should be added that it is easy to forget by directing one's attention away from certain things, and the patient should then be told, by way of example, that on the last occasion he forgot certain events in the trance, and today he will probably forget many, if not all, of them. It should then be suggested to him that he will have a dream before waking, and that as soon as he starts to dream, he will wake up with a start, as if he were awakening from a sound sleep. He should be told that he will remember his dream but forget most, if not all, the other events.

Brenman and Gill (34) describe another procedure intended to produce forgetfulness in the subject during the trance. The subject is told to imagine a board on which he is to write three different words suggested by the hypnotist. He is then told to erase these words from his mind. The words will be erased from his memory and later, when he is asked to reproduce them, he will have to try for a long time and occasionally he may even fail altogether. The hypnotist renews his suggestions of relaxation and drowsiness, and then comes back to the words. Here, as in the preceding tests, it is important to get the subject to agree that the suggestions have had some effect; in the present case, this amounts to getting him to admit that he has had some difficulty in remembering the words. The practitioner goes on from this to tell him that this difficulty will become greater and that finally, he will not be able to remember the words at all. When this stage is reached, the practitioner tells the subject that he is going to count, and that when he comes to a certain number, the words will come back to him — and this is what happens.

The phenomenon which we generally try to induce after amnesia is *post-hypnotic suggestion*. Here again, success naturally cannot be verified until after the end of the trance. The two most readily induced post-hypnotic suggestions are post-hypnotic dreaming and post-hypnotic blinking. To obtain the former, it is suggested to the subject that during the following night he will have a dream which he will remember and relate to the physician at the next session. To induce post-hypnotic blinking, the practitioner tells the subject that he is going to awaken him by counting slowly up to five. At "five", he will open his eyes and look at the practitioner. He will notice that his eyes are blinking and that despite all his efforts, he cannot prevent them from doing so. Then, the subject is informed that the practitioner is going to tell him to close his eyes and is going to count up to three. At "three", he will open his eyes and will notice that this time they are no longer blinking.

A large number of other post-hypnotic suggestions can be be given, provided that care is taken to avoid any of a too fantastic nature. At this stage, the subject may be induced to *speak without waking up*. Some preparation is necessary if the subject, when invited to speak, is not to wake up with a start. We might say to him, for example,

"You are very relaxed, very calm, you are asleep. But although you are asleep, you can talk to me, you can answer my questions without waking up. You will talk like a person talking in his sleep."

The first questions to be asked will be simple ones and will not cause any anxiety. The patient is asked his name and occupation and so on. Later on, he can be trained in the technique of free association and induced to put into words the first idea which comes into his mind.

The next hypnotic phenomenon consists of *positive sensory hallucinations*. Such hallucinations may be induced in very varied forms and constitute the main stock-in-trade of stage-hypnotists, who suggest to their subjects that they are extremely hot, that they are being bitten by gnats and so on. The physician can produce positive sensory hallucinations by using the following suggestions.

"Imagine that we leave this room, you and I. We are in the square of a little town in the south. It is beautiful weather and the sun is shining. I want you to imagine the scene and to raise your hand when you see what I describe. We are in front of a church, the weather is beautiful and you are looking at the church. Can you see it? (*The subject raises his hand.*) You look carefully at the church. You see the steeple. If you see it, raise your hand. Now the bell is going to start ringing. Do you hear it? If you hear it, show me by raising your hand."

"Negative" hallucinations may just as readily be produced. These are characterized by the loss of reality, under hypnotic suggestion, of sensory impressions, such as those involved in the ability to recognize the presence of another person in the room. They indicate a deep trance, in which the subject's eyes may remain open. The *ability to keep the eyes open*, to get up and to walk about indicates a state of complete somnambulism. The behaviour of the subject in this state may be that of a sleep-walker, but in some cases is no different from that of a normal person. To attain this state, the subject must have some preparation. The practitioner may, for example, say to him,

"You are relaxed, you are asleep, deeply asleep. You can open your eyes without waking up. At first, everything will seem confused, and then things will get clearer. You will go on sleeping, and, still asleep, you will be able to get up and walk about just like someone walking in his sleep. Now, open your eyes very slowly. You see things all blurred. But they get more and more distinct and everything now seems quite clear."

The subject can also be told that he will see everything that is pointed out to him. In this way, he will not only be able to see clearly the objects which are actually present, but the vague nature of the suggestions will enable the practitioner to get him to see any kind of imaginary object as well. In this way, hallucinations can be induced in subjects even with their eyes open.

Wolberg (236) describes a technique for training in the ability to experience hallucinations of this kind. He suggests to the subject, while his eyes are still shut, that he sees the hypnotist holding a bottle of water before his eyes. The subject will see the water change colour, turning pink and then gradually turning red. When this happens, he is to lift his left hand gently. The subject is then told that the trance will continue after he has opened his eyes, and that when he opens his eyes, he will see the same things. A real bottle of water is put before the subject's eyes, and he will experience the hallucinatory changes of colour. When he sees the colour changing, he should be given another simple suggestion, for example that he sees a candle burning on the table in front on him.

All the hypnotic phenomena which we have described, up to

the stage of somnambulism, can be induced during the same session if the subjects are first-rate subjects (from 5 to 10 per cent of the normal population). With other subjects several sessions are necessary. It is not, however, essential, for therapeutic purposes, to push the trance as far as this. It may be sufficient to induce inability to lift one's arm and open one's eyes, along with a certain degree of amnesia. With some patients, such as obsessional neurotics who are very difficult to hypnotize, Wolberg recommends that as deep a trance as possible should be obtained during the first session, even if this means taking two hours. These patients are often quite amazed at what is happening to them and do not have time to mobilize their defences during the first session in order to resist induction.

Before leaving the subject of deepening the trance, we may just mention Vogt's method, known as *fractionated hypnosis*. In this method, the patient is awakened several times and re-hypnotized during the same session (225).

Awakening the Patient

BEFORE the subject is awakened, he is given a post-hypnotic suggestion to the effect that at the beginning of the next session, the practitioner will count up to a certain number (five or ten), after which the subject will go into a trance like the one he is in at the moment, or even a deeper one. Instead of numbers, a large variety of other signals may be used to condition the subject's entry into the trance — a word, a phrase, an auditory stimulus like the sound of a bell, or a visual stimulus like a blinking light. The awakening must be done gradually. It should be preceded by suggestions of well-being and rest. The following indicates the kind of procedure to be followed.

"Now, I am going to awaken you. Gradually, you will come out of your trance; I am going to count from five down to one (the reverse order of the previous count). When you wake up, you will feel well and rested and you will feel no unpleasant sensations. You will feel as if you had just had a nap. (These suggestions are repeated). Five, four . . . and so on."

Some subjects, when they wake up, may have a feeling of heaviness in their limbs, nausea and other similar symptoms. The subject may have to be re-hypnotized and given suggestions to make these symptoms disappear. In rare cases, patients may refuse to wake up; some remain in the trance and some fall into a deep natural sleep. The reasons may be different. The former may derive so much gratification from the trance that they do not want it to come to an end. The latter may take refuge in sleep as an escape mechanism before the trance. If the patients do not obey instructions to wake up, which must be firm but never threatening, they should be left alone. They will wake up a few hours later under the stimulus of physiological needs.

The Subject's Experience of the Trance

WHEN the subject has awakened, it is profitable to have a talk with him about his experience during the trance. This talk will also yield information about the depth of the trance. The subject may be left to speak of his own accord, or he may be questioned. Frequently, the subject will say that he has never been asleep.* (In this case, amnesia has evidently not been total.) It may be explained to the patient that hypnotic sleep is not identical with nocturnal sleep, as indeed he had previously been told, and that in hypnotic sleep the subject can hear everything that the hypnotist says. It may be added that, with deep trance states, the subject may forget what has been said during the trance. Care should always be taken to indicate that therapeutic results are not always proportional to the depth of the trance. Again, the subject will often say that he has not been able to carry out all the suggestions. In this case, he may be told that he will do better the next time. Some patients admit that they experienced some of the phenomena suggested, but say that they never lost control over themselves and could have resisted the suggestions if they had wanted to. The answer to this should be that it was never intended, when they were hypnotized, to make them lose control over themselves; but that on the contrary, an increase in this control is highly desirable, and is best shown by voluntary co-operation with the hypnotist.

The subject should then be asked (especially if he is well-educated and capable of self-observation)† to give a detailed

---

*Lassner (personal communication) got the impression from the nineteenth century literature on hypnosis that subjects "slept" much more than they do nowadays. He thinks that the nature of hypnosis may have changed, rather like that of hysteria. This is possible in view of the fact that the authors of the period laid much more stress on the "sleep" aspect of hypnosis. But these authors must be interpreted cautiously. They may have been inclined to over-emphasize this aspect in their accounts.

†Cf. the famous self-observation of the well-known psychiatrist Eugène Bleuler in his article *The hypnotist hypnotised* (in 80).

account of his experience during the trance. The therapist may thus get an idea of the particular way in which the subject has assimilated the experience. He will probably use certain expressions such as, "I plunged, I descended, I was floating" and so on, which the therapist may take up in later sessions.

Hypnosis with Drugs

THE use of drugs to facilitate the induction of hypnosis goes back to the end of the nineteenth century. Chambard (41), in 1881, mentioned the use of ether or chloroform, in weak doses. Hallauer (92), a Berlin obstetrician, in 1922 described the procedure of narco-hypnosis, which consisted of administering a few drops of chloroform at the beginning of induction. He adopted this procedure because of his opposition to hypnosis alone, which he regarded as inopportune. In 1928, although in France hypnosis proper had been under a cloud for thirty years, Brotteaux (38) described the induction of hypnosis under the influence of a mixture of scopolamine (from 0·50 mg to 0·75 mg) and chloralose (from 0·50 g to 0·75 g), which he called scopochloralose.

At a time when it had become socially taboo, hypnosis thus managed to be partially re-introduced because it was associated with a drug, a chemical, not a psychological agent. The procedures which Brotteaux used were of two kinds. In the first of these, he gave the drug, and when the subject showed signs of going to sleep (one to two hours later), he gave direct suggestions, therapeutic or otherwise. In the second, after giving the drug, he waited until the subject became somnolent and then proceeded to orthodox hypnotic induction. After the session was over, the subject was left to sleep for several hours. Brotteaux emphasizes that the therapeutic results are to be attributed to the suggestions given and not to the drug alone. He writes (38), "Eighty per cent of the effect of the drug is due to conscious or unconscious suggestion from the practitioner. Scopochloralose clearly induces a state of suggestibility, but all the resulting effect upon the mind of the patient is due to the influence of the physician."

Baruk and his co-workers (14, 15, 16) who, in addition to Brotteaux, used scopochloralose, on the other hand believed in the therapeutic effect of the drug and used it to remove conversion symptoms. Brotteaux thought that he had succeeded in inducing

122

hypnosis where other methods had failed. But it is not clear whether hypnosis or narcosis is involved here. The same question arises in connexion with the light barbiturate narcosis used in narco-analysis (or narco-synthesis). The question is still controversial. Horsley (97) was able to induce hypnotic phenomena (catalepsy, hallucinations and so on) during light narcosis with sodium pentothal. It is generally agreed that although the states of hypnosis and narcosis may overlap to some extent, they nevertheless remain essentially different. On the psychotherapeutic, interpersonal level, there would appear to be a considerable difference between narco-analysis in which the practitioner uses "armed" intervention, and hypnotherapy in which the hypnotist plays a part which provides more gratification for the subject. The process of regression, in narcosis, is cruder and more brutal, the patient being forced into it, while in hypnosis it is more gradual and allows the defence mechanisms of the personality to come into play (whether in an adaptive or a resistant way).

Hypnosis has been used along with the barbiturates in several ways. Some authors recommend the injection of a weak dose of pentothal and follow this with some form of induction up to the stage of going to sleep. Others use larger doses and carry the induction up to the waking-up stage. Resistant subjects have been successfully hypnotized in this way, and it has been possible, at the next session, to put them into a trance without using drugs at all (60 per cent in Horsley's experiment). Other physicians do not induce hypnosis at all during narcosis, and limit themselves to giving "postnarcotic" suggestions, intended to facilitate hypnosis at the next session.

Without going as far as light narcosis, it may prove helpful to give subjects a weak dose of barbiturate an hour before the session (30 mg of nembutal, for example). This will induce mild somnolence which may facilitate hypnotic induction in these exceptional cases. The taking of the drug has itself a suggestive effect. We have known unsophisticated subjects in whom induction was facilitated by the administration of a placebo. At later sessions, they went to sleep under the influence of the placebo, without the need for verbal suggestion (cf. p. 91).

Specialized Techniques

THE therapeutic applications of hypnosis follow the principles which we have indicated in the first part of the book. They require the induction of a more or less deep trance. If the hypnotist wishes to use hypno-analysis or to devote himself to more elaborate research, specialized techniques have to be acquired. For two of these, the technique of free association and the inducing of dreams or reverie, a light or medium trance is sufficient. The others require a deep trance, if possible somnambulism. We give here a brief outline of the various specialized techniques.

Free association. Here, the subject is told to express every idea or feeling that comes into his head, even if it seems ridiculous or commonplace. The subject may not perhaps succeed in doing this at the first attempt, but he will acquire facility after some practice.

Induction of reverie or dream. It may be suggested to the subject that he is at the theatre. The curtain is down. He is curious to know what is going on behind it. He imagines that, on the stage in front of the curtain there is a man whose face is convulsed with terror. This man is watching what is probably a ghastly scene. The subject wonders why the man is so afraid, and becomes himself imbued with the man's fear. Immediately after, the curtain rises suddenly and the subject sees the scene by which the man was so frightened. He has to describe the scene. After this, the hypnotist again suggests that the subject imagine himself at the theatre, but this time, he has to discover and relate a very pleasant scene. These reveries may provide some information about the patient's conflicts. Afterwards, he should be told to dream about some specific subject relevant to his own anxieties or conflicts. This dream will occur either during the hypnotic session or during the following night.*

*A recent article by Barber (13) reviews experimental work on dreams induced under hypnosis. Barber emphasizes the crucial difference between nocturnal dreams and dreams induced in hypnotized subjects.

Automatic writing. The first step here is to tell the patient, during the trance, that he can write without knowing just what his hand is doing. Then, the hypnotist should suggest to him that a pencil is being placed in his hand and that he is holding the pencil on a sheet of paper, and then that his hand is going to move and begin writing on the paper as if directed by an outside force. Since what the patient writes will be disconnected and as it were in code, he must be trained to translate it. It may be suggested to him that he can open his eyes without waking up and indicate the meaning of what his hand has written; or he may be given post-hypnotic suggestions to enable him to execute automatic writing in the normal waking state. What he writes in this state will naturally have to be translated under hypnosis. Muhl (159) has used automatic writing to recover memories of childhood.

Automatic drawing. Here, the subject is told during a trance that he can open his eyes and make all sorts of drawings on subjects of his own choosing. He is then asked to explain his drawings and to give free associations starting from them.

Play therapy. The patient, who keeps his eyes open, is given lots of toys and asked to use them as he pleases. Sometimes he is also asked to make up stories. This technique may be combined with hypnotic regression (see later).

Crystal and mirror gazing. The patient is told to open his eyes without waking up, and is presented with a crystal ball, a glass of water or a mirror. He is then given suggestions to the effect that when he looks at the object before him, he will see a scene just as if he were at the theatre. He may be left complete freedom in the choice of scene, or he may be told that the scene will have something to do with the problems which bother him. In this way, forgotten memories or situations involving significant persons in his past life may be revived. Muhl (159) and Prince (176) have been particularly concerned with this procedure.

Regression. Here, the patient is taken back to an earlier period of his life. The historical importance of hypnotic regression is well known, since it was in applying the regression technique to his patient Marie that Janet effected a "causal" treatment as distinct from a purely symptomatic treatment. Janet himself started from the work of Bourru and Burot, as we have previously shown (44) (cf. p. 57). The reality of regression remains a controversial question (11, 91, 169, 185, 238). But the technique itself is in current use. With very good somnambulists, it should be enough simply to tell them that they are only this or that age. They will accept the suggestion. But in general, it is better to lead the subject to this stage gradually. The following are the instructions used by Wolberg (237). They are given while the subject is in a deep trance.

"Now, concentrate carefully on what I have to say to you. I am going to suggest that you go back in time, back into the past. You will feel as if you were back in the periods I suggest. Let us start with yesterday. What did you do yesterday morning? What did you have for breakfast? For lunch? Now we are going back to the first day you came to see me. Can you see yourself talking to me? How did you feel? Describe it. What clothes did you wear? Now listen carefully. We are going back to a period when you were little. You are getting small. You are getting smaller and smaller. Your arms and legs are getting smaller. I am someone you know and like. You are between ten and twelve. Can you see yourself? Describe what you see. Now you are getting even smaller. You are becoming very, very little. Your arms and legs are shrinking. Your body is shrinking. You are going back to a time when you were very, very little. Now you are a very little child. You are going back to the time when you entered school for the first time. Can you see yourself? Who is your teacher? How old are you? What are your friends' names? Now you are even smaller than that; you are very, very much smaller. Your mother is holding you. Do you see yourself with mother? What is she wearing? What is she saying?" (237, pp. 212–13).

Erickson describes two other techniques. In the one (66, 67), he begins by disorientating the subject in space and time in order to re-orientate him in a given period of his life. In the other, he induces successive amnesias, removing the subject from the day, week, month and year of his present existence before taking him back to an earlier period of his life.

Induction of experimental conflict. The subject is informed that he will, while asleep, remember something which had previously happened to him and which he had forgotten. He is further told that he will again experience all the same emotions as he experienced on the original occasion. Some imaginary situation is then suggested and the subject is told that after he wakes up, this situation will affect what he does and says, although he will not be aware of this. The subject's reactions to this imaginary situation may provide interesting pointers to the nature of his conflicts and indications for the appropriate therapy.

Newman *et al.* (161) actually combine the two techniques of induced experimental conflict and hypnotic dream.

These specialized techniques are of interest from the experimental point of view. There are as yet no systematic indications for their therapeutic use. In 1947, Brenman and Gill wrote that their "efficacy is largely dependent on the subtle strategies involved" (34, p. 79). For Brenman and Gill, the use of these methods is "dependent almost entirely on the personal intuition of the therapist. It is thus exceedingly difficult to communicate as a hypnotherapeutic approach and remains a more or less unique phenomenon, unrelated to a formulated psychopathology and, accordingly, closer to art than to science. Whereas all of the foregoing is true, to a degree, of all methods of psychotherapy, it seems to be the essential characteristic of this approach" (*ibid.*). In 1959, twelve years later, the same authors remark, "Aside from their usefulness in certain kinds of therapeutic problems, the phenomena resulting from these specialized techniques constitute one of the richest sources we have for studying extremes of the regressive process" (87, p. 334). In addition to the authors just quoted, a particularly ingenious application of most of the specialized techniques is that of Erickson (65, 66, 67) and Erickson and Kubie (68, 69).

Autohypnosis

SUBJECTS who have been hypnotized in the consulting-room sometimes report that they are able to put themselves into a hypnotic state again at home, by imagining that they are back in the setting of the hypnotic session (whether by fixating an object or by imagining that they can hear the hypnotist's voice). In general, these cases finish up by falling into a sleep (during the day or in the evening). Some patients say that they attain the same depth of trance as during the session itself, but the majority report that they reach a less deep trance. These hypnotic states which some subjects can attain unaided may be systematically cultivated in order to consolidate and prolong the effect of symptomatic treatment. Accordingly, patients may be trained in what is called autohypnosis. In autohypnosis in its simplest form, the subject who has been hypnotized during the session with the physician, is told to do the same thing himself at home once or twice per day. Some subjects are able to do so, but the trance is almost always more superficial than that at the session itself. More elaborate training in autohypnosis may be given by several different methods, some under hypnosis with help from the therapist, the others using an autodidactic procedure. Generally speaking, autohypnosis is harder to induce than heterohypnosis. Most frequently, a light or medium trance is obtained. Occasionally, a deep trance may be achieved with the aid of training under hypnosis. The autodidactic methods are considered incapable of producing one.

It may be questioned whether the autohypnosis induced after training under hypnosis should be regarded as genuine auto-hypnosis. In this method, the interpersonal element always plays an important part in the achievement of the trance, and a fundamental part from the point of view of therapy. In the autodidactic method it is apparently absent and consequently the therapeutic effects of this method are doubtful.

It helps in obtaining autohypnosis with training under hypnosis if the subject can achieve a deep heterohypnotic trance. Salter (193) requires as a minimum that the subject should have catalepsy of the limbs or an anaesthesia, but would prefer him to have got as far as a score of 13 on Davis and Husband's scale. The techniques in current use may be of various kinds, of which Weitzenhoffer's (231) may serve as an example. Weitzenhoffer first induces a deep trance, and then gives the following post-hypnotic suggestions.

"Any time in the future that you wish to induce a deep state of hypnosis in yourself, even deeper than the one in which you are now, you will be able to do so. All you will need to do is to place yourself in a comfortable position and relax by taking a few deep breaths and think of relaxing as you did when I hypnotized you a while ago. When you are relaxed, tell yourself mentally that you are going to go into a deep hypnotic state, then take three deep breaths and as soon as you have taken the third breath you will go into a very deep trance. During hypnosis you will be able to think and will have full command of yourself. You will be able to give yourself any suggestion you wish while hypnotized and you will be able to bring about any hypnotic phenomena you desire. To awaken you will only need to tell yourself that you are going to wake up. You will then count to three, and at the last count you will be wide awake. Should any emergency arise when you are hypnotized you will immediately and automatically awaken ready to take whatever action is necessary. Until I tell you otherwise, any time that you have hypnotized yourself, you will always be able to hear me and you will carry out any suggestions I give you, even if they are contradictory to some you have given yourself. But you will not listen to anyone else or accept suggestions from others unless you have previously decided to do so. You will always employ good judgement in using self-hypnosis, and will not use it excessively. You can use it to remove any pains and aches from which you suffer, but you will always consult a physician if they are persistent. You can produce hallucinations if you wish, but you will be careful to do so only when others are not around, or if they are, only if they know what you are doing. You will never give yourself hallucinations that could lead you to harm yourself or others. These suggestions will be effective until I change or remove them. No one else, including you, can change or remove them" (231, pp. 317–18).

Wolberg (236) includes in his hand-levitation method instructions for the achievement of autohypnosis; and Salter (193) describes three techniques adapted to the quality of trance which the subjects are capable of achieving.

The following is an example of autodidactic training, taken from Rhodes (188). According to Rhodes, the subject who wishes to practise autohypnosis should read the following instructions and follow them carefully.

"The first stage of autohypnosis is 'eye closure'. By this I mean a condition in which, although you are awake, you cannot open your eyes. It may be achieved as follows: Sit in a comfortable chair, in a quiet room. Then:
"1. Say *one* and as you say it, think, 'My eyelids are getting very, very heavy.' Repeat that thought, think only that thought, concentrate upon it, mean it, and

believe it as you think it. Exclude any other thoughts such as, 'I'll see if this will
work.' Just repeat the one thought, 'My lids are getting very, very heavy.' If
you think only that thought, concentrate upon it, mean it and believe it as you
think it, your lids will begin to feel heavy. Don't wait until they get very heavy.
When they begin to get heavy, proceed to the next step.

"2. Say *two* and as you say it, think, 'My eyelids are getting so heavy now, they'll
close by themselves.' As in *one,* repeat that thought, think only that thought,
concentrate upon it, mean it, believe it. Do not force your eyes closed, do not
fight to keep them open; just concentrate on the one thought, 'My eyelids are
getting so heavy now, they'll close by themselves,' and as you repeat that thought,
that thought alone, let your eyelids do as they want to. If you really concentrate
on that thought to the exclusion of any other, mean it and believe it as you think
it, your eyelids will slowly close. When your lids are closed, allow them to remain
shut and continue as follows:

"3. Say *three* and as you say it, think, 'My lids are so tightly shut, I cannot open
them no matter how hard I try.' As above, repeat that thought, think only that
thought, concentrate upon it, mean it and believe it. As you do so, try to open
your eyes and you will find that you cannot until you say the word *open*, and then
your lids will pop open.

"Do not be discouraged by failure in your first attempts at self-taught autohypnosis. This is the type of experiment in which the average person will fail the
first two or three times he tries it. That is because the average person has not
learned how to concentrate upon one thought alone, that is, to the exclusion of
all others. This is not due to a lack of intelligence. Indeed, intelligent people
have rather involved thought patterns and are accustomed to thinking more than
one thought at a time. Concentration upon only one thought, to the exclusion of
all others, involves a new discipline, and this requires determination and practice.
So, if you fail the first time, try again. If you are intelligent enough to control
your mental processes, you can succeed in thinking only one thought at a time;
and once you achieve that ability, autohypnosis is in your grasp.

"Thus when your eyes close after *two,* and you go on to *three* and think,
'My lids are so tightly shut, I cannot open them no matter how hard I try,' you
must keep repeating that thought, that thought alone, and as you think it try to
open your eyes.

"As long as you concentrate on that thought alone, your eyelids will remain
shut. Your muscles will strain to open them, but your eyes will remain shut
until you say *open,* either out loud or mentally.

"Once you have achieved eye closure, the next step is to speed up the process.
Try it two or three times to make sure the eye closure is good. Every time you
do it, the effect will be stronger. Now for the acceleration. Do *one* as above, and
the moment your lids get heavy, go on to *two.* As you say *two,* think the requisite
thought only once, or twice at most, but think it exclusively. By now you will
have acquired that ability. As your lids close, say *three,* and again think the requisite thought only once, or twice at most, but think it exclusively. Your lids will
remain shut. Release them by the command, *open.*

"Now go through the procedure once again, but instead of saying *one, two,
three,* just think those numbers, following each one with its appropriate thought.
Finally go through the entire procedure without the numbers; just think the
thought for *one* once, the thought for *two* once, and the thought for *three* once.
With practice you may be able to get almost instantaneous eye closure by merely
letting your lids close and thinking the thought for *three* once.

"You will find that as you acquire speed, you achieve stronger and stronger control. Having mastered the discipline of concentrating upon one simple thought at a time (steps *one* and *two*), you will be able to attain step *three,* a complex thought, almost instantaneously. The touchstone of your success with auto-hypnosis is rapid eye closure. Once you have achieved that, you can proceed to the depth of trance necessary to meet your particular problem or problems.

"The next step is relaxation. Keep your eyes closed, and think, 'I'm going to take a deep breath and relax all over.' Take a *deep* breath, and as you exhale you will relax all over, Think, 'I'll breathe normally and deeply and relax more and more with every breath.' After that, as you breathe, you will relax more and more.

"With good eye closure and relaxation (which in a short time comes with the eye closure), you will have attained the first degree of autohypnotic trance. Your mind is now ready to accept suggestions you make to it with both hypnotic and post-hypnotic effect. But just as in the case of the eye closure itself, where the total rapid result was built up through repetition, so also the succeeding steps sometimes need practice. The secret of success is concentration — the ability to think one thought at a time, to the exclusion of all others, and to mean and believe it.

"Try simple suggestions first. For example: Grasp your left index finger with your right hand fist. Think, 'I cannot pull my finger out.' As above, concentrate on that thought alone, mean it, believe it, and as you think it, try to pull your finger out. It will remain stuck until you think, 'Now I can release it,' or use some other word or phrase with similar import" (pp. 251–3).

Rhodes then gives a number of other simple suggestions which can be used in the same way, such as arm rigidity, hand clasp, illusion of warmth and so on.

Group Hypnosis

GROUP hypnosis consists of hypnotizing several subjects at the same time. It should not be confused with group psychotherapy proper, for group psychotherapy is non-directive and in it the members maintain free relationships with each other and with the group leader. As far back as the end of the eighteenth century, the age of animal magnetism, Mesmer and Puységur worked with groups of patients. Nearer to our own time, at the beginning of the present century, group hypnosis was widely used by Wetterstrand (233), Van Renterghem (222) and others. The first advantage of group hypnosis is that it saves time. For example, groups of pregnant women may be prepared by the hypno-suggestive method (Ambrose and Newbold, 4; Kroger and Freed, 122; Doniguevitch, 62; and Zdravomyslov, 239). Some Soviet obstetricians have even created "hypnotariums" for this purpose (Syrkine, 218; Vigdorovitch, 223). The method is also used in the treatment of alcoholics, especially in the United States and in the countries of Eastern Europe. Group hypnosis also serves experimental ends by facilitating the selection of good subjects; and enables the hypnotizability of some members of the group to be increased, at first by providing the example of better subjects and later by enabling them to benefit from the support which the group itself provides.

Group hypnotherapy has limited results. It is of a directive nature and includes elements of support and persuasion. The technique used does not differ essentially from that used in individual hypnosis. The therapist may, for example, proceed as follows. When the subjects have taken their seats, and have closed their eyes, he gives them successive suggestions of relaxation, heaviness, sleep and so on. He then tells them to open their eyes. The subjects who have responded best to the suggestions are taken out in front of the rest of the group. They are given suggestions to relax, close their eyes and go into a deep trance. When the therapist has obtained several deep trances, he holds these up as examples to the other members. He assures the latter that they also can achieve the same results and that if they will make another attempt, they will find it easy to go into a deep sleep. At this point the therapist should renew the suggestions which he has already made, and almost always, some of the subjects who have so far resisted sleep will go into a deeper trance. Each of them will subsequently be more readily hypnotized during an individual session.

Hypnodrama

UNLIKE group hypnosis, hypnodrama is a genuine form of group psychotherapy. It combines hypnosis and psychodrama. This is not the place to describe Moreno's well-known psychodrama technique. It is enough merely to observe that it is a form of psychotherapy which, by using a kind of improvised dramatic performance on a given theme, enables a subject to externalize his conflicts in action, and in some measure to integrate them. In addition to the subjects, psychodrama involves the director or leader of the performance (one of the therapists) and the auxiliary egos or other protagonists in the drama (the other therapists). The performance takes place on a stage, before an audience. In hypnodrama the subject is previously hypnotized by the director.

Moreno thinks that, already in Mesmer's time, the "group factor" was an integral part of psychotherapy. Since then, it has been neglected, but Moreno sees it making its re-appearance in hypnotherapy. With Enneis, he has described the technique of hypnodrama (156). The disadvantage of hypnodrama is that it is available only to the best somnambulists.

We have reviewed above the main techniques of hypnotherapy. In our view, what we have said is enough to give an idea of its application, in so far as this is possible without actual demonstration. Those who would like to know more about the techniques may consult the following references: Wolberg (236), Weitzenhoffer (231), Brenman and Gill (34), Schultz (200), Stokvis (213), Schilder and Kauders (197), Erickson (70) and Kroger (123). Wolberg, in fact, was the first to codify (in 1948) modern hypnotic techniques in his *Medical Hypnosis* (236), and we have made considerable use of his work. Those who are particularly interested in anaesthesiology should consult Marmer (145) and Lassner (129, 130). For obstetrics, reference should be made to

Zdravomyslov (239), Kroger and Freed (122), Ambrose and Newbold (4), August (6) and Clark (51), and for dentistry, to Moss (157) and Shaw (204).

PART THREE

TECHNIQUES DERIVED
FROM HYPNOSIS

Techniques Derived from Hypnosis

HYPNOTHERAPY has had to contend from the start with three basic problems.

1. *Hypnotizability*. The degree of hypnotizability was found to vary from one person to another, and some subjects proved to be completely intractable.

2. *Manner of application*. The question arose how hypnosis could be applied so as to serve therapeutic ends.

3. *The doctor-patient relationship*. This relationship played a very important part and its management had to be considered.

Attitudes toward these three problems have often led to the creation of techniques derived from hypnosis, as we shall attempt to show.

Hypnotizability.

This question was of little interest during the "animal magnetism" period, for the essential factor was the transmission of the beneficial fluid. It acquired greater importance in the "suggestion" period and contributed largely to the creation of new techniques. Since not everyone was hypnotizable, attention was directed toward techniques by which one individual could exert influence over another without hypnosis being necessary.

Manner of Application.

This again raised no problems during the animal magnetism period. The fluidist theory implied physical contact between patient and therapist. The latter, with the aid of passes, transmitted the beneficial force to his patient. He also used physical agents like Mesmer's "baquets" (tubs) and Puységur's magnetized trees. All practitioners of hypnosis were not necessarily physicians at this time. With the introduction of verbal suggestion at the end of the nineteenth century, the practice of psychotherapy became more the business of physicians who began to consider the question of the manner of application. The removal of symptoms by direct suggestion no longer satisfied them, and Bourru and Burot (1888, cf. p. 57) were the first to introduce a "causal" treatment involving regression with return to the past on the part of the patient, during which he re-lived the emotions which he had experienced at the time when the illness began. They did use the "crisis", but paid most attention to the verbal and emotional content. Janet (1889) discovered his method while verifying the work of Bourru and Burot. Breuer was already using this "return to the past" in 1881,* but his joint publication with Freud appeared only in 1893 (35). On the whole, hypnotherapy was limited to direct suggestion. Freud became bored with the repetitiveness of the procedure. He tried the cathartic method, but came up against the difficulty that everyone could not be hypnotized.† He then modified his technique. He placed his hand on the subject's forehead, without hypnotizing him, and urged him to talk. Later, he abandoned physical contact and his directive attitude and hit upon the technique of free association. It is unnecessary to say any more about this technique or the future which awaited it.

Some contemporary hypnologists have retained the procedure of hypnotizing, but in addition to direct suggestion and the cathartic method, also employ other techniques, which we have described in our chapter on *Specialized Techniques*. Some even combine classic hypnosis with the free association technique. This technique, known as hypno-analysis, is still, as we have seen, at the experimental stage.

J. H. Schultz (201) has also modified the classic hypnotic technique in the form of his *Autogenic Training,* an autohypnotic technique in which direct suggestion is replaced by exercises. These exercises, six in number, are practised in a certain order to obtain successively a feeling of heaviness, a feeling of warmth, the perception of the cardiac and respiratory rhythm, a sensation of warmth in the epigastric region and a sensation of cold on the forehead. We cannot give any further details of the technique here. Reference may be made to the book by Schultz and Luthe

---

* Miss Anna O. at first did it spontaneously, so that she is said by some to be the one who discovered the cathartic method.

†In the belief that his technique was inadequate, he went to Nancy in 1889· to perfect it.

(201), to the symposium *La Relaxation* (184) and to the proceedings of the first French language congress of psychosomatic medicine held in Vittel in 1960 (54).

Starting from this technique of Schultz, Kretschmer developed the technique of "graduated active hypnosis". The interested reader may refer to Kretschmer's own book (120), to two articles, one by Kretschmer himself (121) and one by his pupil Langen (127), and to Langen's recent book (128). Stokvis, another author inspired by Autogenic Training, has described a technique called Active Control of Muscular Tone (211).

Some of Schultz's followers (for example, Kurth) combine the practice of hypnosis with that of Autogenic Training. The subject practises the exercises at home and is then hypnotized when he comes to see the therapist. Other exponents of Autogenic Training regard this combination as inadmissible. Kurth* uses the combined treatment in the following way with patients who accept the principle of suggestive therapy. He first of all teaches them the first of Schultz's exercises (heaviness of the right arm) which they practise for eight to fifteen days. At the next consultation, he tells them that while they are with him they are to practise a more complex exercise which they cannot do by themselves. He then begins by suggesting the sensation of heaviness and warmth all over their bodies, and in this way often induces hypnotic sleep. The patients continue to practise the usual exercises at home, while on their visits to the therapist they undergo global hetero-suggestive hypnosis.

We should not pass on without mentioning the *Coué method,* which was developed at the beginning of the century, at the time when hypnosis came under a cloud. After enjoying a great popularity, it fell into oblivion. For details of this method, the reader should consult the books of Coué (55) and Baudoin (17), which did much to make it known.

Doctor-patient Relationship.

The nature of the interpersonal relationship in hypnosis and its use for therapeutic purposes has received very varied interpretations, in which irrational as well as rational factors have played a considerable part. Authors, consciously or

---

*Personal communication.

unconsciously, were confronted with the "intense" and "wild" transference to which Henri Ey refers in his Foreword to the present book. Very soon its importance for treatment was understood, whether it was called, according to the period, "rapport", "suggestion", or "transference". An attempt was made to "civilize" this "wild" transference and to use it in a more rational manner. As Henri Ey remarks, "It is not surprising that the development of this immediate transference into a controlled process extending over time, and the use of language for communication between therapist and patient led Freud to his discovery."

Transference also produced counter-transference reactions which had the effect of increasing motivation toward modifying the technique. Such modifications were not only to mean an improvement in technique, but were also to have the effect of keeping the patient at a certain distance. This gave the therapist some security and enabled him on the one hand to take a more objective attitude toward the patient and on the other hand to bring into action the defences and resistances on the basis of which depth therapy could be practised. In this way, restructuring of the personality was made possible, and this increased the effectiveness of treatment.

The importance of "sympathy" in hypnosis has been observed and reported ever since hypnosis was discovered. "Rapport" was already involved in Mesmer's procedures. All the magnetizers of the nineteenth century were well aware of the existence of interpersonal relationships and described them quite fully. Jones' book (107) and de Saussure's article (195) contain many references on the subject.

This emotional relationship, implying as it does interpersonal involvement, has played a very large part in the development of psychotherapy. Resistances to this emotional involvement, while they have impeded the advance of psychotherapy, have at the same time brought certain benefits. For one thing, they have contributed to the development of drug therapy; for another, it may well be that they have, in a quite unforeseen way, led to fundamental discoveries in psychotherapy, such as the notion of transference.

If scientific psychotherapy is taken as starting in the Mesmer period, this is because the question of interpersonal relationship was then for the first time studied experimentally, in particular by the Academies of the period in their famous report on animal magnetism in 1784. The purpose of the Academicians' investigation was to establish the existence of a physical causal factor, the fluid. Since they found no evidence for this, they concluded that there was no such thing as magnetism. Their report describes the phenomena occurring in consequence of the interpersonal relationship, without making any attempt to probe them any further. The Secret Report (181), however, emphasizes the erotic aspect of these phenomena and this might explain the Academicians' reticence toward the whole matter. In this report, we actually find the following passage:

"Women are always magnetized by men. The relations thereby established are doubtless only those of a patient with her doctor, but the doctor is a man. Whatever the nature of the illness, it does not deprive us of our sex, nor completely remove us from the other's power" (pp. 93–94).

The magnetic "séance" is described thus:

"Frequently the man ... passes his right hand behind the woman's body; each leans towards the other to facilitate this contact. They get as close as possible, their faces almost touching: their breaths mingle, all their physical impressions are immediately shared, and it is inevitable that the mutual attraction of the sexes should operate with its full force. It is not surprising that the senses become inflamed. The imagination, also operative, spreads an element of disorganization through the whole system; it catches the judgement unawares and diverts the attention; the women cannot take proper account of their feelings, and are unaware of the state they are in" (p. 95).

The secret report concludes, "Magnetic treatment cannot but be a moral danger" (p. 96).

Mesmer himself was not unaware of the interpersonal ties between himself and his patients. "Animal magnetism", he wrote, "must in the first place be transmitted by feeling. Feeling alone can make the theory intelligible. For example, one of my patients, who is used to experiencing the effects which I have upon him, has an additional propensity for understanding me compared with other men."

Mesmer, however, instead of resorting to some kind of psychological explanation, persisted in retaining the idea of a fluid. The fluidist theory allowed the therapist some degree of "depersonalization". It invoked the intervention of a "third force" in, and at the same time outside of, the therapist, who was but the vector of this universal force.

Mesmer rejected the verbal relationship which accompanied the introduction of somnambulism. No doubt, in his case, this rejection represented a defence mechanism. The distinction of having been the first to use verbal communication as a therapeutic procedure belongs to Puységur. But this discovery may well have been partly a result of unconscious motivation, and it is possible that for Puységur, speech effected a degree of distance in relation to the patient, and thus afforded another form of defence. It should be remembered that in our own time, psychoanalytically oriented writers have emphasized that speech may accentuate the separation from others (cf. 160).

Certain contemporaries and followers of Mesmer, however, had already shown some reserve concerning the fluid, and minimized its importance. These "voluntarists" held that to obtain results with a patient, one had to *want* to cure him, and to *love him*. Of particular significance here is the work published by one of Puységur's disciples, Charles de Villers,* and entitled *Le Magnetiseur Amoureux* (224), in which, under the guise of fiction, he expounds his ideas, to the effect that the positing of a fluid is unnecessary, that magnetism consists of the "firm will" to cure the patient and that the efficacy of the doctor depends upon an attitude compounded of cordiality and love.

One cannot fail to see, behind the spiritualistic language of Villers, the anticipation of ideas advanced in our own time by certain psychoanalysts concerning the curative factors in their method. They hold that even correct interpretations lose their efficacy if they are not backed by an unconscious attitude similar to that foreshadowed by Villers. For example, in Villers we find,

---

* Charles de Villers was an artillery officer, like Puységur (and also Laclos, the famous author of *Liaisons Dangereuses*). Officers at this time had a penchant for magnetism and found excellent subjects among their men. As Louis Figuier wrote in his *Histoire du Merveilleux* (1860), "Magnetizing, with all its charms, appeared to have become the principal occupation of military life. This was the golden age of the private."

The writer would like to express his thanks to Dr. Raymond de Saussure for having drawn his attention to the rare work quoted, of which there is a copy in the library of the Medical School at Besançon.

"The soul of the magnetizer unites with that of the somnambulist, which is thereby identified with his own" (op. cit., p. 123). The view expressed here may be compared with that indicated by Nacht, "We all acknowledge that the analysts' interventions are fruitful in as much as he succeeds in communicating with the patient's unconscious—to the point of literally being able to 'put himself in the patient's place' while remaining in his own" (160).

For Villers, one's power over the patient "will depend... on the greater or lesser degree of harmony of our inner dispositions, and particularly on the cordiality with which I can infuse my will" (op. cit., p. 124). Similarly, Nacht considers that "the analyst's attitude, when it is one of *unconditional* kindness, becomes then, and only then, that support and strength necessary to the patient to conquer the fear which bars the way to recovery" (160).

Finally, Villers' fictional work is full of pronouncements on the primary role of love. For example, "I carry within me that which is necessary to relieve my fellow. The most sublime part of my being is devoted to this purpose; and it is in this feeling of the most tender solicitude that my friend is sure to find a remedy for his ills" (op. cit., p. 114).

Here again, it is impossible not to see the similarity between this and the following passage from Nacht, "No one can cure another if he has not a genuine desire to help him; and no one can have the desire to help unless he *loves*, in the deepest sense of the word." These dispositions are in part innate. But Nacht considers that "this attitude is possible only when the analyst has been able to reduce to a minimum within himself the inevitable, eternal ambivalence of man" (160). This should of course be the result of a good personal analysis of the therapist himself. It need scarcely be said that today the position of the psychoanalyst in the therapeutic relationship with his patient is also different in view of his awareness and his skill in the management of the transference and counter-transference.

It appears, from what has been said above, that certain of Mesmer's disciples, and especially Villers, were aware of the element of interpersonal involvement. Villers himself gave full attention to the erotic forms which this involvement can take in some cases, and warned against the dangers to which it might lead. But, unlike the Academicians, he did not on that account refuse to study the interpersonal relationship involved in magnetism. He accepted involvement in the relationship, but only partial involvement. Although it may be true that Villers had some idea of this relationship as a "contact of inner disposition" between two individuals, and that others after him spoke of the feeling of confidence and even, in some cases, of the attachment which the patient could experience in relation to his doctor, the therapist nevertheless played, for him, the essential role in the therapeutic process. It is true of Villers as of other magnetizers of this period, whether they believed in the action of the will alone, or in the combined action of the will and the fluid. We may therefore agree with de Saussure that it is as if the transference originated not with the patient, but with the physician wishing to cure him.

This assumption of a one-way relationship by the magnetizers might also be interpreted as a defence and as a resistance on their part to complete two-way involvement. The therapist thus protected himself against the affective demonstrations of the patient, keeping a degree of distance. (It is interesting to find that even at the physical level, a modification of technique was introduced. Direct contact with the patient's body by way of passes gave way to passes kept at a certain distance from the patient's body.)

Despite a certain partial receptiveness to interpersonal involvement on the part of certain magnetizers at the beginning of the nineteenth century, resistances, on the whole, continued in evidence. At the close of the nineteenth century, well-known physicians who took up hypnosis were still unwilling to accept their own involvement in the therapist–patient relationship. To avoid the psychological concept of suggestion, they invented metallotherapy, which introduced an intervening physical agent (again a relic of fluidism). But even the physicians who accepted involvement in the psychotherapeutic process showed some unconscious resistance which paradoxically sometimes actually facilitated the progress of psychotherapy. Freud's discovery of transference may perhaps be explained in this way. There was the famous episode of the patient who showed her amatory inclinations toward Freud, and the scare which this gave the latter. He refused to attribute the incident to his "own irresistible personal attractions". He presumably preferred to "depersonalize" himself, casting himself in the role of substitute for the person really loved by the patient. This interpretation of the situation would thus be a starting-point for the development of the theory of transference (although the patient may well have been physically attracted to Freud).

It is well known that Breuer had had a similar experience with one of his patients, the famous Anna O., and had, as a result, abandoned the study of hysteria. Jones remarks that Freud, in order to get Breuer to take it up again, told him of his own patient "flinging her arms round his neck in a transport of affection", and explained "his reasons for regarding such untoward occurrences as part of the transference phenomena" (107, p. 275).

Szasz (219) has recently examined the defensive aspect of transference, and observes, "The threat of the patient's eroticism was effectively tamed by Freud when he created the concept of transference." In Szasz's view, Freud elaborated this concept in relation to what happened to Breuer; not being personally involved in the matter, he was able to view it more dispassionately and found an explanation. In our view, however, the emotional basis for Freud's elaboration of the concept of transference is to be found in his own experience, i.e., in the episode to which we have referred above. For if, as Szasz says, the function of the concept of transference was for Freud, among other things, to protect against the patient's eroticism, it seems more plausible to believe that he hit upon it in circumstances where he felt himself to be personally a target.

Whatever the defensive nature of transference may be, the fact remains that Freud abandoned hypnosis. He was to rediscover transference in his new technique. Fenichel emphasizes that "Freud was at first surprised when he met this phenomenon" (75, p. 29). We may wonder whether Freud experienced this surprise when he was using hypnosis, or when he was using the new technique. What Fenichel says does not answer this question. The bibliographic reference which he gives is to an article entitled "The dynamics of the transference" (1912), which does not mention the surprise which Fenichel claims that Freud experienced. Freud did, however, express himself in the following terms in his article "On the history of the psychoanalytic movement":

"It may thus be said that the theory of psychoanalysis is an attempt to account for two *striking and unexpected*** facts of observation which emerge whenever an attempt is made to trace the symptoms of a neurotic back to their sources in his past life: the facts of transference and resistance" (84a, p. 16).

Fenichel may perhaps have been thinking of this passage. Freud does in fact refer in it to something which he found surprising, but the passage quoted gives no clear indication of the circumstances in which this surprise appeared *for the first time.* However that may be, Freud accepted transference, in spite of his surprise, and thus started a new era in psychotherapy.

If the relation between hypnosis and transference is complex, that between transference and suggestion is equally so. The concept of suggestion has never been adequately defined, and Ida Macalpine (141) observes of transference that "the mechanism of transference and its mode of production seems particularly little understood". She remarks that the psychoanalytic literature relevant to this "mode of production" is very scanty, and that there is only one single reference to it in Fenichel's (75) bibliography of 1646 items.

Ida Macalpine emphasizes that the new technique of psychoanalysis tended to repudiate the idea of suggestion, but that we find Freud re-introducing it a little later. "We have to admit," he says, "that we have only abandoned hypnosis in our methods in order to discover suggestion again in the shape of transference" (84, p. 373). Elsewhere he writes, "We can easily recognize it (i.e., transference) as the same dynamic factor that the hypnotists have named 'suggestibility', which is the agent of hypnotic rapport . . ." (81, p. 76); and again, "It is perfectly true that psychoanalysis, like other psychotherapeutic methods, employs the instrument of suggestion (or transference). But the difference is this; that in analysis it is not allowed to play the decisive part in determining the therapeutic results" (op. cit., p. 77). In his *Introductory Lectures on Psycho-analysis* (84), Freud used the terms "transference" and "suggestion" indiscriminately, but emphasized that direct suggestion had been abandoned. He insists that suggestion (or transference) is used differently in psychoanalysis from the way in which it is used in other forms

---

*Our italics.

of psychotherapy. In psychoanalysis the transference is continually being analysed and resolved. Suggestion is thus eliminated by the resolution of the transference. Ida Macalpine thinks that although this is quite true, it does not explain either transference or suggestion. She writes, "... it is dubiously scientific to include in the definition of suggestion the subsequent relation between therapist and patient; neither is it scientifically precise to qualify 'suggestion' by its function: whether the aim of suggestion be that of covering up or uncovering, it is either suggestion or it is not. Little methodological advantage could be gained by using 'suggestion' to fit the occasion, and then to treat the terms 'suggestion', 'suggestibility' and 'transference' as synonymous. It is therefore not surprising that the understanding of analytic transference has suffered from this persisting inexact and unscientific formulation" (141, p. 507).

She later gives her own definition. "If a person with a certain degree of inherent suggestibility is subjected to a suggestive stimulus and reacts to it, he can be said to be under the influence of suggestion. To arrive at a definition of analytic transference, it is necessary first to introduce an analogous term for suggestibility in hypnosis and speak of a person's inherent capacity or readiness to form transferences. This readiness is precisely the same factor and may be defined in the same way as suggestibility, namely, a capacity to adapt by regression. Whereas in hypnosis the precipitating factor is the suggestive stimulus, followed by suggestion, in psychoanalysis the person's adaptability by regression is met by the outside stimulus (or precipitating factor) of the infantile analytic setting. In psychoanalysis it is not followed by suggestion from the analyst, but by continued pressure to further regression through the exposure to the infantile analytic setting. If the person reacts to it, he will form a transference relationship, i.e., he will regress and form relations to earlier images. Analytic transference may thus be defined as a person's gradual adaptation by regression to the infantile analytic setting" (op. cit., pp. 532–3).

The problem of the relations between suggestion, transference and hypnosis becomes even more complex when psychophysiological concepts are added to those which have so far remained purely psychological, instinctual and motivational. Such an attempt at synthesis has been made, as we have previously seen,

by Kubie and Margolin (125) and Gill and Brenman (87). A
new dimension has been added. Physical manipulation — some
sort of sensory deprivation — in itself and independently of transference, provokes regressive behaviour, both physical and
mental.

Another fruitful attempt to eliminate suggestion has been
made by the German author J. H. Schultz. Without completely
giving up hypnosis, he developed a modified technique which he
called *Autogenic Training* or "passive concentration". He
trains his subjects in fractionated autohypnosis, so that they can
reach "a state of beneficial relaxation analogous to sleep without
the need for any suggestion from outside" (202). The technique
is therefore one of hypnosis without hetero-suggestion. Schultz
agrees with the observations that a subject in a hypnotic state
experiences sensations of heaviness and warmth, the former of
which indicates muscular relaxation and the latter vasodilatation.
The first two exercises in his method therefore consist of learning
to feel these two sensations. Relaxation, which has generally
been regarded as an epiphenomenon of hypnosis is, for Schultz,
the essential factor. It is relaxation which produces the change
of attitude (Umschaltung). Schultz regards both hypnosis and
his own method as forms of "organismic" psychotherapy in
contrast to the "mental" forms of psychotherapy. The latter,
which include psychoanalysis, operate in the field of intellect
and instinct. The organismic methods make no attempt on the
patient's personality but seek to collaborate with him in effecting
a change of attitude. "Somatization" is the guiding principle of
these organismic methods and "consists in getting the individual
to withdraw from the outside world by fixating some monotonous stimulus, or closing his eyes, and then to concentrate
with intensity on his own physiological functions and identify
with them . . . Mental functions are also considerably modified . . .
the outside world and external reality recede, thoughts become
visions, etc., mental functions slow down, all just as in sleeping
and dreaming" (202). We do not wish to imply that Autogenic
Training is simply a form of suggestive hypnosis. It is, on the
contrary, a well-codified technique which introduces new
elements not found in heterohypnosis or even in autohypnosis
as it is usually practised, i.e., by the deliberate use of suggestion.
The transference (and counter-transference) relationship between

patient and doctor is "damped" by the exercises, which create a degree of distance reassuring to the two participants in the exchange. Autogenic Training may thus be taught to therapists with a less elaborate training in psychotherapy than is required to practise hypnosis. Autogenic Training, however, cannot on any account be reduced to mere practice of the exercises. It is a form of psychotherapy, as Schultz insists; and he even restricts the right to use it to physicians. But it seems to us that theoretically it is still incomplete with respect to the interpersonal element and the occurrence of transference. For Schultz, the theoretical problem is quite simple. Since he regards relaxation as the very essence of hypnosis, his theory of autohypnosis presents no particular difficulties for him. But those who do not accept his explanation of hypnosis are not likely to be wholly satisfied with his theoretical explanation of Autogenic Training.

When we read the account of relaxation quoted above and interpret it in the light of the most recent psychoanalytic theories of hypnosis (87, 124), we cannot but be struck by the fact that it includes all the regressive physical and mental elements to be found in suggestive hypnosis. It remains to be seen whether transference always accompanies these states. It has been seen that as far as hypnosis is concerned, opinions vary. Gill and Brenman seem to think that it does. Kubie allows that transference may be absent in some cases, but he does not specify under what conditions. Would such conditions be met by Autogenic Training? Why is it that one form of regression is accompanied by an archaic relationship while another is not? A more thorough theoretical account of the role of the interpersonal factor in Autogenic Training is required.

Ajuriaguerra and Michèle Cahen (3) have undertaken relevant research by attempting to apply psychoanalytic concepts and the ideas of transference and regression in the interaction of patient and therapist at the level of muscle tone. They are trying to establish what new dimension the controlled exercise of this "muscular communication" (resistances manifesting themselves by muscular tension) introduces into the psychotherapeutic relationship.

It is difficult to know whether the subjective experience is the same or different in hypnosis and Autogenic Training. We started to treat a patient with an irritable bladder by Autogenic Training.

She proved to be a good subject and her condition improved somewhat. In an attempt to increase the effectiveness of treatment, we used classic hypnosis, presented not as a more intense form of the exercises, as by Kurth, but as a different procedure. At the visit after the one at which she was hypnotized, the patient told us that she found her exercises harder to do, but that she felt a constant amelioration. During this same session, she was able to do the exercises again, and was also successful later at home. But she still distinguished two different subjective experiences. The question is whether this distinction was due to the fact that we presented the two experiences to her as being different, or whether two intrinsically different subjective experiences were involved. This is a complex problem of subjective experience to which it is difficult to find an answer. Thorough clinical investigations might throw a certain amount of light on the matter, but it would not be easy to define it objectively.

The notion of "Umschaltung" or change of attitude introduced by Schultz with reference to hypnosis as well as Autogenic Training, is an interesting conception of the same kind as that of the "trigger" and transitional processes advanced by Kubie. The ideas of physiological lability put forward by Vedenski and by Oukhtomski may be regarded in some ways as similar attempts to understand the nature of hypnosis (in 207).

Conclusion

WE HAVE now reached the end of our task, and we should be the last to claim that the account of hypnosis which we have given is an exhaustive one. We have been unable to go into as much detail as we should have liked, and have had to pass rapidly over a number of areas, particularly the physiological* and psychological studies which have been made of hypnotic phenomena. Although, however, the book has not dealt with everything, we hope that we have done sufficient to convince the reader that, whatever some people, especially in France, may think, hypnosis is by no means a thing of the past. This does not mean that we have tried, as H. Faure (74), in something of an overstatement, puts it, "to re-forge the link between one aspect of contemporary French psychiatry and the methodological source from which it has been trying so hard and so misguidedly to free itself since the beginning of the century". More modestly, we have endeavoured to show, in historical perspective, the claims of hypnosis to a place of importance as the source of modern psychotherapy.

At the present time, there is no all-embracing theory of hypnosis. Neurophysiological studies do not yet provide us with a sufficiently solid basis for such a theory. The Pavlovian school has opened up new prospects for research, and its contribution has certainly not been unfruitful, even though no definitive answer has yet been found. The very fact that a school whose point of view is basically materialist recognized the existence of hypnosis, hitherto surrounded by something of a mystical halo, did much to remove this halo.

The contributions of experimental psychology have likewise failed to provide a final answer. But thanks to them, the problem can now be seen more clearly, and it may be possible, as Orne

---

*A consideration of this question is to be found in the articles by Gorton (88), Crasilneck and Hall (56) and Deckert and West (60), and a critical review is included by Barber (12).

153

believes, by successively eliminating every "artifact" of hypnosis, finally to approach its "essence" (165).

Psychoanalytic explanations of hypnosis have followed the development of psychoanalytic theory in general. First, the emphasis was on libidinal factors and the Oedipus stage (76, 82, 196), next on the pregenital stage (75, 78), then on ego psychology (19, 33), and finally, on the importance of aggression in the dynamics of the hypnotic relationship (210). All these psycho-analytic approaches open new perspectives, but do not resolve the problem of the specific nature of the hypnotic state. The various factors referred to are present in all psychotherapeutic relationships. But even if, while throwing light on the psycho-dynamics operating in the relationship, they fail to provide the final key to the nature of hypnosis, they do nevertheless enable us better to understand a vital aspect of it, the relational or inter-personal aspect, which is of special importance in the thera-peutic use of hypnosis. The psychoanalytic theories may be said to illuminate the "substructures", just as the theories derived from experimental psychology illuminate the "superstructures".

We have still to discover the nature of the specific distinguish-ing factor in hypnosis. In Kubie's (124) view, "there is nothing remarkable about the psychological ingredients in the phenom-enology of hypnotism, nothing to differentiate them from their manifestations in other psychological states, whether normal or pathological. What is peculiar for hypnotism is the psycho-physiological setting which makes possible their special con-sequences". This means that we must turn to inter-disciplinary research for light on hypnosis. This kind of research is of vital importance if it is true, as Charcot at the end of the last century and Kubie at the present time have emphasized, that hypnosis provides a path to the understanding of mental illness. We may remind the reader that at the present time, in our society, mental illness and cancer constitute the two main areas in medicine in which more knowledge is urgently required. It is advisable to delimit the field of research with great care and to reconsider the concepts proper to its study. Standing as it does on the border between physical and mental, hypnosis offers an exciting prospect for psychosomatic research. Furthermore, in view of its power to modify states of consciousness, hypnosis has also a role to play in research in psychopathology. Yet again, hypnosis, in its crude form, provides an intense psychotherapeutic relationship, in which psychological and physiological concomitants operate in a particularly clear way. It is therefore at the very least a technique capable of showing up an interpersonal relationship in a relatively isolable form. When the difficulties of any research in interpersonal psychology are taken into consideration the hypnotic technique as such may very well appear to offer an exceptional tool for research. Finally, hypnosis is a therapeutic procedure which, when used in a knowledgeable way, may be added to the arsenal of psychotherapeutic weapons. It has proved itself highly fruitful in the past and still merits the attention of contemporary workers.

Bibliography

1. ABOULKER, P. and CHERTOK, L. Emotional factors in stress incontinence. *Psychosomatic Med.*, 1962, 24, 507–10.
2. AJURIAGUERRA, J. DE and GARCIA BADARACCO, J. Les thérapeutiques de relaxation en médecine psychosomatique. *Presse médicale*, March 1953, 61, 316–20.
3. AJURIAGUERRA, J. DE and CAHEN, M. Tonus corporel et relation avec autrui. L'expérience tonique au cours de la relaxation. *Rev. Méd. Psychosom.*, 1960, 2, 89–124.
4. AMBROSE, C. and NEWBOLD, G. *A Handbook of Medical Hypnosis.* Baillière, Tindall and Cox, London, 1956, 255 pp.
5. AUERBACK, A. and SMITH, D. R. Functional Diseases, pp. 1–57 in Functional disturbances, vol. XII, 312 pp. *Encyclopedia of Urology*, Springer, Berlin-Göttingen-Heidelberg, 1960.
6. AUGUST, R. V. *Hypnosis in Obstetrics.* McGraw-Hill, New York, 1961, 160 pp.
7. BABINSKI, J. *De l'hypnotisme en thérapeutique et en médecine légale.* Imprimerie de la Semaine médicale, Paris, 1910, 15 pp.
8. BACHET, M. and PADOVANI, P. Réflexions sur le traitement psychothérapique des douleurs des amputés. *Ann. méd.-psychol.*, 1951, 102, 206–11.
9. BACHET, M. Note préliminaire concernant l'emploi en thérapeutique humaine des méthodes provoquant des inhibitions de type hypnotique. Confrontation avec les idées exprimées par Pavlov dans ses leçons sur l'activité du cortex cérébral. *Ann. méd.-psychol.*, 1951. 109, 557–63.
10. BACHET, M. Inhibition de type hypnotique et inhibition par l'ambiance en thérapeutique psychosomatique. *Gaz. méd. France.* 1953, 7, 847–60.
11. BARBER, T. X. Hypnotic age regression: a critical review. *Psychosom. Med.*, May–June 1962, 24, 286–99.
12. BARBER, T. X. Physiological effects of "hypnosis". *Psychol., Bull.* 1961, 58, 390–419.
13. BARBER, T. X. Toward a theory of hypnotic behaviour: The hypnotically induced dream. *J. Nerv. Ment. Dis.*, 1962, 135, 206–21.
14. BARUK, H. L'association scopolamine-chloralose. Action physiologique expérimentale et essais thérapeutiques en neuropsychiatrie. *Gaz. méd. Fr.*, Jan. 1935, 6, 39–43.
15. BARUK, H., GEVAUDAN, MLLE, CORNU, R. and MATNEY, J. Action vasculaire du scopochloralose. Quelques mécanismes physiologiques de ses effets thérapeutiques dans l'hystérie. *Ann. méd.-psychol.*, 1936, 94, 187–94.
16. BARUK, H. and MASSAUT, C. Action physiologique expérimentale et clinique du scopochloralose. *Ann. méd.-psychol.*, 1936, 94, 702–12.
17. BAUDOIN, C. *Suggestion and Autosuggestion.* Trans. by E. and C. PAUL. Allen and Unwin, London, 1920, 288 pp.

158 BIBLIOGRAPHY

18. BEAUNIS, H. *Le somnambulisme provoqué*. Baillière, Paris, 1887, 292 pp.
19. BELLAK, L. An ego-psychological theory of hypnosis. *Int. J. Psycho-Anal.*, 1955, **36**, 373–9.
20. BERNHEIM, H. *Suggestive Therapeutics*. Trans. from 2nd ed. by C. A. HERTER. Pentland, Edinburgh, 1890, 420 pp.
21. BERNHEIM, H. Le Docteur Liébeault et la doctrine de la suggestion. *Revue médicale de l'Est* 1907, **39**, pp. 36–51; 70–82.
21a. BERNHEIM, H. *Automatisme et suggestion*, Felix Alcan, Paris, 1917, 165 pp.
22. BEXTON, W. H., HERON, W. and SCOTT, T. H. Effects of decreased variation in the sensory environment. *Canadian J. Psychol.*, 1954. **38**. 70–76.
23. BIRMAN, B. M. *Experimental Sleep (Experimentalni Son)*, with a preface by I. P. PAVLOV. State Publishing House, Leningrad, 1925, 65 pp. (in Russian).
24. BODNER, H., HOWARD, A. M., KAPLAN, J. H. and ROSS, S. C. Hypnosis in office practice, especially in the practice of urology. *Postgrad. Med.*, Nov. 1960, 515–8.
25. BONAPARTE, MARIE L'homme et son dentiste. *Rev. franç. de Psychanal.*, 1933, **6**, 84–88
26. BONFILS, S. and LAMBLING, A. Quelques problèmes psychosomatiques particuliers posés par l'ulcère gastro-duodénal. L'optique du somaticien et de l'expérimentateur. pp. 112–23 in *Psychosomatique et Gastro-Entérologie*. Masson et Cie, Paris, 1962.
27. BOUL N. I. *Hypnosis and Suggestion in Internal Medicine. (Gipnoz I Vnushenie V Klinikie Vnutrennik Boleznie)*. Medguiz, Moscow, 1958, 185 pp. (in Russian).
28. BOURRU, H. and BUROT, P. *Les variations de la personnalité*. Baillière, Paris, 1884, 314 pp.
29. BOWERS, M. K. Theoretical considerations in the use of hypnosis in the treatment of schizophrenia. *Int. J. clin. exper. Hypnosis*, 1961, **9**, 39–46.
30. BRAID, J. *Neurypnology*. Churchill. London, 1843, 265 pp.
31. BRAMWELL, J. M. *Hypnotism, its History, Practice and Theory*. Grant Richards, London, 1903. Re-issued by Julian Press, New York, 1956, 271 pp.
32. BRENMAN, M. The Phenomena of Hypnosis. p. 125 in *Problems of Consciousness*. Josiah Macy Jr. Foundation, New York, 1951, 200 pp.
33. BRENMAN, M., GILL, M. M. and KNIGHT, R. P. P. Spontaneous fluctuations in depth of hypnosis and their implications for ego-function. *Int. J. Psycho-Anal.*, 1952, **33**, 22–33.
34. BRENMAN, M. and GILL, M. *Hypnotherapy*. International Universities Press, New York, 1947, 276 pp.
35. BREUER, J. and FREUD, S. *Studies in Hysteria*. (Trans. by A. A. BRILL). Nervous and Mental Disease Pub. Co., New York, 1950.
36. BRODIE, D. A. and HANSON, H. M. A study of the factors involved in the production of gastric ulcers by the restraint technique. *Gastroenterology*, 1960, **38**, 353–60.
37. BROTTEAUX, P. *Hypnotisme et scopochloralose*. Paris, Vigot frères, 1936.
38. BROTTEAUX, P. Hypnotisme et scopochloralose dans les interventions chirurgicales. *Revue Métapsychique*, 1938, **2**, 111–17.
39. BROWN-SÉQUART. C. E. *Recherches expérimentales et cliniques sur l'inhibition et la dynamogénie; application des connaissances fournies*

par ces recherches aux phenomènes principaux de l'hypnotisme et du transfert. Masson et Cie., Paris, 1882, 32 pp.

40. BURQ, V. *Des Origines de la Metallothérapie.* Delahaye et Lecrosnier, Paris, 1883, 142 pp.

41. CHAMBARD, E. Du Somnambulisme en général. Doin, Paris, 1881, 140 pp.

42. CHARCOT, J. Oeuvres complètes Delahaye et Lecrosnier, Paris, 1885–90, 9 vols.

43. CHERTOK, L. Sommeil hypnotique prolongé. pp. 57–60 in *La cure de sommeil,* Masson et Cie, Paris, 1954, 238 pp.

44. CHERTOK, L. À propos de la découverte de la méthode cathartique. *Bull. Psychol.,* Numéro spécial en hommage à P. Janet, 5 Nov. 1960, 33–37. Abridged version in English. On the discovery of the cathartic method. *Int. J. Psychoanal.,* 1961, **42,** 284–7.

45. CHERTOK, L. and CAHEN, MURIEL Facteurs transférentiels en hypnose. *Acta psychother* (Basle), 1955, suppl., vol. 3, 334–42.

46. CHERTOK, L. and KRAMARZ, P. Hypnosis, sleep and EEG, *J. nerv. ment. Dis.,* 1959, **128,** 227–38 (bibliography).

47. CHERTOK, L. "Hypnose et suggestion" in *Encyclopédie médico-chirugicale.* Volume de psychiatrie, 2, 1955, **37,** 810. E, 10, 1–7 (bibliography).

48. CHERTOK, L. *Psychosomatic Methods in Painless Childbirth.* Trans. by D. LEIGH. Pergamon Press, London and New York, 1959, 260 pp.

49. CHERTOK, L. Hypnose animale. pp. 447–66 in (71).

50. CHERTOK, L., ABOULKER, P., CAHEN, M., Perspective psychosomatique en urologie. *Évolut. psychiat.,* 1953, **3,** 457–73.

51. CLARK, R. N. A training method for hypnotic childbirth. pp. 219–43 in COOK, C. E. and VAN VOGT, A. E. *The Hypnotism Handbook,* Griffin Publishing Company, Los Angeles, 1956, 243 pp.

52. *Congrès (premier) International de l'Hypnotisme expérimental et thérapeutique,* Octave Doin, Paris, 1889, 367 pp.

53. *Congrès (deuxième) International de l'Hypnotisme expérimental et thérapeutique. Tenu à Paris du 12–18 août 1900.* Vigot Frères, Paris, 1902, 320 pp.

54. *Congrès (premier) de Médecine Psychosomatique de langue française. Revue Méd. psychosomat.,* 1960, **2,** 2 and 3.

55. COUÉ, E. *Self Mastery through Conscious Autosuggestion.* Allen and Unwin, London, 1922, 92 pp.

56. CRASILNECK, H. B. and HALL, J. A. Physiological changes associated with hypnosis. *Int. J. clin. exp. Hypnos.,* 1959, **1,** 9–50.

57. CRASILNECK, H. B., STIRMAN, J. A., WILSON, J. B., McCRANIE, E. J., and FOGELMAN, M. J. Use of hypnosis in the management of patients with burns. *J. Amer. med. Ass.,* 1955, **158,** 102–6.

58. CUVELLIER, A. *L'école hypnologique de Nancy,* 1866–1926. Thesis, Nancy, 1953, 207 pp.

59. DAVIS, L. W. and HUSBAND, R. W. A study of hypnotic suggestibility in relation to personality traits. *J. abnorm. soc. Psychol.,* 1931, **26,** 175–82.

60. DECKERT, G. H. and WEST, L. J. Hypnosis and experimental psychopathology. *J. clin. Hypnosis,* 1963, **5,** 256–76.

61. DESLON, M. *Observations sur le Magnétisme animal.* P. Fr. Didot, Le Jeune, Paris, 1780, 151 pp.

62. DONIGUEVITCH, M. I. *The Psychoprophylactic Method of Painless*

Childbirth (Metod Psikhoprofilaktiki Boliei v Rodakh.) Gosmedgizdat, Kiev, 1955, 172 pp. (in Russian).

63. DORCUS, R. M. *Hypnosis and its Therapeutic Applications.* McGraw-Hill, New York, 1956.

64. ERICKSON, M. H. Hypnosis, general review. *Dis. nerv. Syst.,* Jan. 1941, **2,** 13–18.

65. ERICKSON, M. H. The applications of hypnosis to psychiatry. *Med. Rec.,* 1939, **150,** 60–65.

66. ERICKSON, M. H. A study of clinical and experimental findings on hypnotic deafness. *J. gen. Psychol.* 1938, **19,** 127–50; 151–67.

67. ERICKSON, M. H. The induction of color blindness by a technique of hypnotic suggestion. *J. gen. Psychol.,* 1939, **20,** 61–89.

68. ERICKSON, M. H. and KUBIE, L. S. The use of automatic drawing in the interpretation and relief of a state of acute obsessional depression. *Psychoanal. Quart.,* 1938, **7,** 443–66.

69. ERICKSON, M. H. and KUBIE, L. S. The successful treatment of a case of acute hysterical depression by a return under hypnosis to a critical phase of childhood. *Psychoanal. Quart.,* 1941, **10,** 583–609.

70. ERICKSON, M. H., HERSHMAN, S. and SECTER, I. I. *The Practical Application of Medical and Dental Hypnosis.* Julian Press, New York, 1961, 470 pp.

71. EY, H. *Psychiatrie animale.* Desclée et Brouwer, Paris, 1964, 605 pp.

72. FARIA, L'ABBÉ DE. *De la cause du sommeil lucide.* Jouve, Paris, 1905, 362 pp. Re-issue of the 1819 edition.

73. FAURE, H. and BURGER, A. Sur un cas d'eczéma rebelle disparu en deux séances d'hypnose. *Le Progrès Médical,* 10 Sept., 1954, **17,** 339–40.

74. FAURE, H. À propos de: Les méthodes psychosomatiques d'accouchement sans douleur de L. Chertok. *Évolution Psychiatrique,* no. IV, 1957, 771–82.

75. FENICHEL, O. *The Psychoanalytic Theory of Neurosis.* Kegan Paul, Trench, Trubner, London, 1946, 703 pp.

76. FERENCZI, S. Introjection and transference. pp. 39–93 in *First Contributions to Psychoanalysis.* Hogarth Press, London, 1952, 338 pp.

77. FISHER, C. Hypnosis in treatment of neuroses due to war and other causes. *War Medicine,* 1943, **4,** 565–76.

78. FISHER, C. Studies on the nature of suggestion: Part I, Experimental induction of dreams by direct suggestion. *J. Amer. psychoanal. Ass.,* April 1953, **1,** 222–55. Part II, The transference meaning of giving suggestions, *ibid.,* 406–37.

79. FOISSAC, P. *Rapports et Discussions de L'Académie Royale sur le Magnétisme animal.* Baillière, Paris, 1833, 559 pp.

80. FOREL, A. *Hypnotism, or Suggestion and Psycho-therapy.* Trans. from 5th German ed. by H. W. ARMIT. Rebman, London and New York, 1906, 370 pp.

81. FREUD, S. *Autobiographical Study.* Hogarth Press, London, 1927, 137 pp.

82. FREUD, S. *Group Psychology and the Analysis of the Ego.* Hogarth Press, London, 1940, 134 pp.

83. FREUD, S. A short account of psychoanalysis. pp. 191–209 in *Complete Psychological Works,* vol. XIX, Hogarth Press, London, 1961.

84. FREUD, S. *Introductory Lectures on Psychoanalysis,* 2nd ed. Allen and Unwin, London, 1933.

84a. FREUD, S. On the history of the psychoanalytic movement, in *Complete Psychological Works,* vol. XIV, Hogarth Press, London, 1961.

85. FREUD, S. Turnings in the ways of psychoanalytic therapy. Address delivered before the Fifth International Psycho-Analytical Congress in Budapest, September 1918. pp. 392–402 in *Collected Papers*, vol. 2. Hogarth Press, London, 1924.

86. GAUTHIER, AUBIN, *Histoire du somnambulisme*. Felix Malteste et Cie., Paris, vol. I, 454 pp., vol. II, 440 pp.

87. GILL, M. and BRENMAN, M. *Hypnosis and Related States*. International Universities Press, Inc., New York, 1959, 405 pp.

88. GORTON, B. E. Physiologic aspects of Hypnosis, pp. 246–80, in Schneck (198).

89. GRINBERG, L. Relations between psycho-analysts. *Int. J. Psycho-anal.* 1963, 44, 362–7

90. GUÉGUEN, J. L'accouchement sous hypnose (méthode et résultats). *Gynec. et Obstet.*, 1962, 61, l, 92–113.

91. HADFIELD, J. A. The reliability of infantile memories. *Brit. J. med. Psychol.*, 1923, 13, 87–111.

92. HALLAUER, B. Die Hypnose in der Gynaekologie und Geburtshilfe und die Narkohypnose. *Zbl. Gynaek.*, 11 Nov. 1922, 45, 1793–808.

93. HARTMANN, H. Ich Psychologie und Anpassungsproblem. *Int. Z. Psychoanal.*, 1939, 61–135. English translation: *Ego Psychology and the Problem of Adaptation*. Imago Publishing Co. Ltd., London, 1958. 121 pp.

94. HELD, R. Le dentiste et son patient. *Rev. franç. d'Odontostomat.*, 1958, 10, 1935–42.

95. HELD, R. Variations de la technique psychanalytique classique. *Encycl. Méd. Chir. Psychiatrie*, 11–1960. 37812 C30.

96. HILGARD, I. R., HILGARD, E. R. and NEWMAN, H. M. Sequelae to hypnotic induction with special reference to earlier chemical anaesthesia. *J. Nerv. Ment. Dis.*, 1961, 133, 462–78.

97. HORSLEY, J. S. *Narcoanalysis*. London, Oxford University Press, 1943, 134 pp.

98. HORVAI, I. *Hypnosis in Medicine (Hypnosa v Lekarstvi)*. State Medical Publications, Prague, 1959, 319 pp. (in Czech.).

99. HULL, C. L. *Hypnotism and Suggestibility, an Experimental Approach*. Appleton Century Co., New York, 1933, 416 pp.

100. ILLOVSKY, J. Experiences with group hypnosis on schizophrenics. *J. ment. Sci.*, 1962, 108, 685–93.

101. ISRAËL, L. and ROHMER, F. Variations electroencéphalographiques au cours de la relaxation autogène et hypnotique. pp. 89–98 in (184).

102. IVANOV-SMOLENSKI, A. G. The mechanization of the hypnotic process (Opyt mekanizatsii gipnotitshkovo vozdieistvia). *Vratchebnoie Dielo*, 1928, 3, 221–4 (in Russian).

103. JANET, P. *L'automatisme psychologique*. Alcan, Paris, 1921, 9th ed., 491 pp. (1st ed. 1889).

104. JANET. P. *Principles of Psychotherapy*. Trans. by H. M. and E. R. GUTHRIE. Macmillan, New York, 1924; Allen and Unwin, London 1925, 322 pp.

105. JANET, P. *Psychological Healing. A Historical and Clinical Study*. Trans. by E. and C. PAUL. 2 vols. Macmillan, New York; Allen and Unwin, London, 1925, 1265 pp.

106. JELTAKOV M. M., SKRIPKIN I. K. and SOMOV B. A. *Electrical Sleep and Hypnosis in Dermatology (Electroson I Guipnoz v Dermatologii)*. Medguiz, Moscow, 1963, 308 pp.

107. JONES, E. *Sigmund Freud: Life and Work*. 3 vols. Hogarth Press London, 1953–7.

108. JONES, E. The nature of auto-suggestion. *Brit. J. med. Psychol.*, 1923, **3**, 206–12.

109. JONES, E. *Papers on Psycho-Analysis*. Baillière, Tindall and Cox, London, 5th ed. 1948. 504 pp.

110. JUSSIEU, A. L. DE Rapport de l'un des commissaires chargés par le Roi de l'examen du Magnétisme animal. Veuve Hérissant, Paris, 12 September 1784; 51 pp.

111. KARTAMISHEV, A. I. *Hypnosis and Suggestion in the Treatment of Skin Diseases (Guipnoz i Vnoushenie v Terapii Koshnykh Bolesniei)*. Medguiz, Moscow, 1953, 135 pp. (in Russian).

112. KAUFMAN, M. R. and BEATON, L. E. A psychiatric treatment program in combat. *Bull. Menninger Clin.*, 1942, **11**, 1–14.

113. KAUFMAN, M. R. Hypnosis in psychotherapy today. Anachronism, fixation, regression or valid modality. *Arch. gen. Psychiat.*, 1961, **4**, 30–39.

114. KENNEDY, A. The medical use of hypnotism. *Britt. med. J.*, 8 June 1957, **1**, 1317–19.

115. KING, P. Hypnosis and schizophrenia. *J. nerv. ment. Dis.*, July-Sept. 1957, **125**, 431–6.

116. KLEMPERER, E. Hypnotherapy. *J. nerv. ment. Dis.*, Aug. 1947, **106**, 176–85.

117. KLINE, M. *Hypnodynamic Psychology*. Julian Press, New York, 1955, 367 pp.

118. KOPIL-LEVINA, Z. A. Analgesia in childbirth through verbal suggestion. (Metodika Obezbolevainia Rodov slovesnim vnusheniem.) pp. 34–65 in PLATONOV, K. I. *Problems of Psychotherapy in Obstetrics* (Voprossi Psykhoterapii v Akusherstvie). Kharkov, 1950 (in Russian).

119. KONSTOROUM, S. *Practical Psychotherapy (Opyt Prakticheskoi Psikhoterapii)*. Ministry of Health of the R.S.F.S.R. Institute of Psychiatry, Moscow, 1959, 223 pp. (in Russian).

120. KRETSCHMER, E. *Psychotherapeutische Studien*. Thieme Verlag, Stuttgart, 1949, 215 pp.

121. KRETSCHMER, E. Hypnose fractionnée active, pp. 99–108 in (184).

122. KROGER, W. S. and FREED, S. C. *Psychosomatic Gynaecology: Including Problems of Obstetrical Care*. Saunders, Philadelphia, 1951, 503 pp.

123. KROGER, W. S. *Clinical and Experimental Hypnosis*. J. B. Lippincot Co., Philadelphia and Montreal, 1963, 361 pp.

124. KUBIE, L. S. Hypnotism. A focus for psychophysiological and psychoanalytic investigations. *Arch. gen. Psychiat.*, 1961, **4**, 40–54.

125. KUBIE, L. S. and MARGOLIN, S. A physiological method for the induction of states of partial sleep, and securing free association and early memories in such states. *Trans. Amer. neurol. Ass.*, 1942, 136–9.

126. KUBIE, L. S. and MARGOLIN, S. The process of hypnotism and the nature of the hypnotic state. *Amer. J. Psychiat.*, March 1944, **100**, 611–22.

127. LANGEN, D. Méthode de l'hypnose fractionnée. pp. 109–19 in (184).

128. LANGEN, D. *Anleitung zur gestuften Aktivhypnose*. Georg Thieme, Stuttgart, 1961, 47 pp.

129. LASSNER, J. Hypnose et anesthésie. *Anésth. et Analg.*, Dec. 1954, **9**, 789–807.

130. LASSNER, J. L'hypnose en anesthésiologie. *Cah. Anésth.*, July 1960, **7**, 741–66.

131. LASSNER, J. Hypnose und Hypno-Narkose bei ambulanten Kranken. *Die Therapiewoche*, 1962, **12**, 1057–60.

132. LEBEDINSKI, M. S. *Outline of Psychotherapy (Otcherki Psikhoterapii).* Medguiz, Moscow, 1959, 350 pp. (in Russian).
133. LEVY, M., VELLEY, CL. and BORGIDA, J. Prevention de l'ulcère de contrainte et essais de traitement de l'ulcère humain par des injections de noyaux de mitochondries et microsomes d'hypothalamus. *Arch. Mal. App. dig.,* 1960, **49**, 1301–6.
134. LIBERSON, W. T., SMITH, R. W. and STERN, A. Experimental studies of the prolonged "hypnotic withdrawal" in guinea pigs. *J. Neuropsychiat.,* 1961. **3**, 28–34.
135. LIÉBEAULT, A. A. *Du sommeil et des états analogues considérés surtout au point de vue de l'action du moral sur le physique.* Masson et Cie, Paris, 1866, 535 pp.
136. LIÉBEAULT, A. A. *Étude sur le zoomagnétisme.* Masson et Cie, Paris, 1883, 29 pp.
137. LIÉBEAULT, A. A.*Thérapeutique suggestive,* Paris, O. Doin, 1891, 308 pp.
138. LIFCHITZ, S. IA. *Hypnoanalysis of Traumata in Hysterics (Guipnoanaliz Infantilnikh Travm ou Isterikov).* Moscow, 1927, 79 pp. (in Russian).
139. LILLY, J. C. Mental effects of reduction of ordinary levels of stimuli on intact healthy persons. *Psychiatr. Res. Reports.,* 1956, **5**, 1–9.
140. LINDNER, R. M. Hypnoanalysis as a technique of psychotherapy. Ch. 2, pp. 25–37 in BYCHOWSKI, G. and DESPERT, J. L. *Specialised Techniques in Psychotherapy.* Evergreen Books, New York, 1958, 371 pp.
141. MACALPINE, I. The development of the transference. *Psychoanal. Quart.,* 1950, **19**, 501–39.
142. McDOUGALL, W. *Outline of Abnormal Psychology.* Charles Scribner's Sons, 1926.
143. MAHON, P. A. O., Examen sérieux et impartial du magnétisme animal. London, Paris, Royer, 27 July, 1784; 43 pp.
144. MARGOLIN, S. Psychotherapeutic principles in psychosomatic practice. In WITTKOWER and CLEGHORN: *Recent Developments in Psychosomatic Medicine.* Pitman, London, 1954.
145. MARMER, M. H. *Hypnosis in Anesthesiology.* Thomas, Springfield, Ill., 1959, 142 pp.
146. MASON, A. A. *Hypnotism for Medical and Dental Practitioners.* Secker and Warburg, London, 1960, 223 pp.
147. MEARES, A. *A System of Medical Hypnosis.* Saunders, Philadelphia and London, 1960, 484 pp.
148. MEARES, A. An atavistic theory of hypnosis. pp. 75–87 in (220).
149. *Meeting of the two Academies on the physiological teaching of Pavlov (Sessia dvukh Akademii posviashtsionnaia fiziologuitcheskomu Utcheniu Pavlova).* Verbatim Proceedings. U.S.S.R. Academy of Sciences, Moscow, 1950, 734 pp. (in Russian).
150. MENNINGER, K. *Theory of Psychoanalytic Technique.* Basic Books, New York, 1958, 179 pp.
151. MESMER, F. A. *Mesmerism . . . Being the first translation of Mesmer's historic Mémoire sur la découverte du magnétisme animal to appear in English* (By V. R. MYERS). Macdonald, London, 1948, 63 pp.
152. MESMER, F. A. *Précis historique des faits rélatifs au magnétisme animal.* London, 1781, 229 pp. (translated from German).
153. MESMER, F. A. *Mémoire de F. A. Mesmer sur ses découvertes.* Fuchs, Paris, an VII, 110 pp.
154. MONTASSUT, M., CHERTOK, L. and GACHKEL, V. À propos d'une amnésie hystérique, traitée par l'hypnose. *Ann. Méd.-Psychol.,* 1953, **111**, 207-12.

164 BIBLIOGRAPHY

155. MONTSERRAT-ESTEVE, S. L'Hypnose pendant les cinq dernières années (1955–60). *Acta psychothér.*, 1961, 9, 429–68.
156. MORENO, J. L. and ENNEIS, J. M. *Hypnodrama and Psychodrama.* Beacon House, New York, 1950, 56 pp.
157. MOSS, A. A. *Hypnodontics. Hypnosis in Dentistry.* Dental Items of Interest Publishing Co., Brooklyn, 1952, 292 pp.
158. MOULINIÉ, Ch. Lettre sur le magnétisme animál, adressée à Monsieur Perdriau, Pasteur et Professeur de l'Église et de l'Académie de Genève, par Charles Moulinié, ministre du Saint-Evangile, Paris, 24 April, 1784, 25 pp.
159. MUHL, A. M. Use of automatic writing in determining conflicts and early childhood impressions. *J. abnorm. Psychol.*, 1923, 18, 1–32.
160. NACHT, S. The curative factors in psycho-analysis. *Int. J. Psycho-anal.*, 1962, 43, 206–11.
161. NEWMAN, R., KATZ, J. and RUBENSTEIN, R. The experimental situation as determinant of hypnotic dreams. *Psychiatry,* Feb. 1960, 23, 63–73.
162. NICOLAIEV, A. P. *Theory and Practice of Hypnosis from the Physiological Point of View (Teoria i Praktika Guipnoza v Fizzologuitcheskom Osveshtchenii).* Kiev, 1927, 64 pp. (in Russian).
163. OBERMAYER, M. *Psychocutaneous Medicine.* Thomas, Springfield, Ill., 1955, 487 pp.
164. ORNE, M. Implications for psychotherapy derived from current research on the nature of hypnosis. *Amer. J. Psychiat.*, 1962, 118, 1097–103.
165. ORNE, M. The nature of hypnosis: Artifact and essence. *J. abnor. social Psych.*, 1959, 58, 277–99.
166. PARCHEMINEY, G. Quelques aspects du problème de l'hypnose. *Évolut. psychiat.*, 1932, 3, 77–90.
167. PATTIE, F. A. Theories of Hypnosis, in (63).
168. PAVLOV, I. P. *Twenty Years of Experiment in the Objective Study of Higher Nervous Activity in Animals (Dvatzatiletni Opyt Obiektivnova Isutchenia Vysshei Nervnoi Dieiatelnosti Shivotnikh).* Medguiz, Moscow, 1951, 485 pp. (in Russian).
169. PLATONOV, K. I. On the objective proof of the experimental personality age regression. *J. gen. Psychol.*, 1933, 9, 190–209.
170. PLATONOV, K. I. *Suggestion and Hypnosis in the Light of Pavlov's Theories (Vnoushenie i Guipnoz v Svete Outchenia I. P. Pavlova).* Medguiz, Moscow, 1951, 53 pp. (in Russian).
171. PLATONOV, K. I. La parole en tant que facteur physiologique et thérapeutique, Leçon 2, pp. 41–63 in Velvovski et al. *Psychoprophylactic Analgesia in Childbirth (Psikhoprofilaktika Boliei V Rodakh).* Medguiz, Leningrad, 290 pp. (in Russian). French translation of Lesson 2, Commissions de Gynec., Obstetr. et de Neuropsychiatrie France-U.S.S.R., 1955, 25 pp.
172. PLATONOV, K. I. *The Word as a Physiological and Therapeutic Factor.* Foreign Languages Publishing House, Moscow, 1959, 452 pp. (in English).
173. POROT, A. *Manuel alphabétique de Psychiatrie.* Presses Universitaires de France, 1952, 437 pp.
174. POUTILINE, S. A. Treatment of a severe case of the herpetiform dermatosis of pregnancy (Guipnoterapia tiasholovo guerpetiformnovo dermatoza beremennosti). *Vop. Okhrany Materin. Dets.*, 1961, 10, 90–91 (in Russian).
175. PRINCE, M. *The Unconscious,* Macmillan Co., New York, 1914, 549 pp.

176. PRINCE, M. Automatic writing combined with crystal gazing. *J. abnorm. Psychol.*, 1925–26, **20**, 34.

177. PUYSÉGUR, A. M. J. MARQUIS DE. *Mémoires pour servir à l'histoire et à l'établissement du magnétisme animál*. London, 1785, 256 pp.

178. PUYSÉGUR, A. M. J. MARQUIS DE. *Appel aux savants observateurs du dix-neuvième siècle de la décision portée par leurs prédécesseurs contre le magnétisme animál et fin du traitement du Jeune Hebert*. Dentu, Paris, 1813, 127 pp.

179. *Rapport des Commissaires de la Société Royale de Médicine nommées par le Roi pour faire l'examen du magnétisme animál*. Imprimerie royale, Paris, 1784, 39 pp.

180. *Rapport des Commissaires chargés par le Roi de l'examen du magnétisme animál*. Imprimerie royale, Paris, 1784, 66 pp.

181. Rapport secret sur le magnétisme animal redigé par Bailly au nom des commissaires chargés par le Roi, pp. 92–100 in BURDIN, G. JEUNE et DUBOIS (d'Amiens), FRÉD. *Histoire académique du magnétisme animál*. Bailière, Paris, 1841, 651 pp.

182. *Reflexions impartiales sur le magnétisme animál*, faites après la publication du rapport des commissaires chargés par le Roi de l'examen de cette découverte. Genève, Chirol; Paris, Périsse 1784, 50 pp. Pamphlet attributed to Marquess Ant. de Dampierre (Barbier).

183. *Regarding Hypnosis:* Statement of Position by the American Psychiatric Association, 15 Feb. 1961. Central office of the APA, Washington.

184. *Relaxation, La* Ed. by P. ABOULKER, L. CHERTOK and M. SAPIR. Expansion Scientifique Française, Paris, 3rd ed. 1964, 320 pp.

185. REIFF, R. and SCHEERER, M. *Memory and Hypnotic Age Regression*. Int. Universities Press, Inc., New York, 1959, 253 pp.

186. Report of the British Medical Association Committee. *Brit. med. J. Supplement,* 23 April 1955.

187. Report of the American Medical Association Committee. *J. Amer. med. Ass.,* 1958, **168**, 185–9.

188. RHODES, R. H. *Curative Hypnosis*. Elek Books, London, 1952, 274 pp.

189. ROBERTSON, G. M. The use of hypnotism among the insane. *J. ment. Sci.,* 1893, **39**, 1–12.

190. ROJNOV, V. E. *Hypnosis in Medicine (Guipnoz v Meditsine)*. Medguiz, Moscow, 1954, 116 pp. (in Russian).

191. ROSEN, H. Hypnosis. Applications and mis-applications. *J. Amer. med. Assoc.,* 1960, **172**, 683–7.

192. ROSEN, M. and BARTEMEIER, L. H. Hypnosis in medical practice. *J. Amer. med. Assoc.,* 1961, **175**, 976–9.

193. SALTER, A. *What is Hypnosis? Studies in Auto- and Hetero-conditioning*. Athenaeum Press, London, 1950, 95 pp.

194. SARBIN, T. R. Contributions to role-taking theory. I. Hypnotic behaviour. *Psychol. Rev.,* 1950, **5**, 255–70.

195. SAUSSURE, R. DE, Transference and animal magnetism. *Psychoanal. Quart.,* 1943, **12**, 2.

196. SCHILDER, P. *Ueber das Wesen der Hypnose*. Springer, Berlin, 1922, 32 pp. English translation, *The Nature of Hypnosis*, International Universities Press, New York, 1956, Pt. 1, 7–41.

197. SCHILDER, P. and KAUDERS, O. *Lehrbuch der Hypnose*, Springer, Berlin and Vienna, 1926. English translation, *The Nature of Hypnosis*. International Universities Press, New York, 1956, Pt. 2, 45–184.

198. SCHNECK, J. M. *Hypnosis in Modern Medicine.* Thomas, Springfield, Ill., 1953, 323 pp.
199. SCHNECK, J. M. Hypnoanalysis. *Int. J. clin. exp. Hypnos.*, 1962, **10**, 1–12.
200. SCHULTZ, J. H. *Hypnose-Technik.* 4th ed. Gustav Fisher, Stuttgart, 1959, 81 pp.
201. SCHULTZ, J. H. *Das Autogene Training* (Konzentrative Selbstenspannung). Thieme Verlag, Stuttgart, 1956. English version, SCHULTZ, J. H. and LUTHE, W. *Autogenic Training.* Grune and Stratton, New York; Heinemann, London, 1959, 289 pp.
202. SCHULTZ, J. H. Sur le problème de la somatisation dans la psychothérapie. *Rev. méd. psychosom.*, 1960, **2**, 85–87.
203. SCHWARTZ, O. *Psychogenese und Psychoterapie, koerperlicher Symptome.* Springer, Wien, 1925, 481 pp.
204. SHAW, I. *Clinical Applications of Hypnosis in Dentistry.* Saunders, Philadelphia and London, 1958, 173 pp.
205. SIDIS, B. *The Psychology of Suggestion.* D. Appleton-Century, New York, 1898.
206. SINCLAIR-GIEBEN, A. H. C. Treatment of status asthmaticus by hypnosis. *Brit. med. J.*, 3 Dec. 1960, 1651–2.
207. SLOBODNIAK, A. P. *Psychotherapy, Suggestion and Hypnosis (Psikhoterapia, Vnoushenie, Guipnoz).* State Publishing House UK.S.S.R. Kiev, 1963, 379 pp. (in Russian).
208. SOLOMON, P., KUBJANSKY, P., LEIDERMAN, P., MENDELSON, J., TRUMBULL, R. and WEXLER, D. (eds.) *Sensory Deprivation. A Symposium held at Harvard Medical School.* Harvard U. P., Cambridge, Mass., 1961, 262 pp.
209. SPEER, E. *Der Arzt der Persoenlichkeit. Ein Lehrbuch der aerztlichen Psychotherapie.* Thieme, Stuttgart, 1949, 285 pp.
210. STEWART, H. A comment on the psychodynamics of the hypnotic state. *Int. J. Psycho-Anal.*, July 1963, **44**, 372–4.
211. STOKVIS, B. La régulation active du tonus musculaire envisagée comme thérapie de décontraction. pp. 71–80 in (184).
212. STOKVIS, B. Allgemeine Ueberlegungen zur Hypnose. pp. 71–121 in FRANKEL, V. E., GEBSATTEL, V. E. VON and SCHULTZ, J. H. *Handbuch der Neurosenlehre und Psychotherapie.* Urban und Schwarzenberg, Munich and Berlin, 1957.
213. STOKVIS, B. *Hypnose in der arztlichen Praxis.* Karger, Basel, 1955, 336 pp.
214. STOKVIS, B. Results of psychotherapy. *Top. Probl. Psychother,* 1960, **1**, 64–72, Karger, Basel.
215. SVIADOSHTSH, A. M. *The Neuroses and their Treatment (Nevrozi i ikh Lietchenie).* Medguiz, Moscow, 1959. 364 pp. (in Russian).
216. SVORAD, D. *Animal Hypnosis.* (Paroxysmalni Utlm). Slovak Academy of the Sciences, Bratislava, 1956 (in Slovak).
217. SVORAD, D. and HOSKOVEC, J. Experimental and clinical study of hypnosis in the Soviet Union and the European socialist countries (bibliography). *Amer. J. clin. Hypnosis,* July 1961, **4**, 36–46.
218. SYRKINE, M. M. Three years at the Kiev obstetric hypnotarium. (Dosvid paboti Kievskovo misskovo akousherskovo guipnotariiou za 3 roki). *Pediat. Akush. Ginec.*, 1950, **1**, 28–30 (in Ukrainian).
219. SZASZ T. S. The concept of transference. *Int. J. Psycho-anal.*, 1963, **44**, 432–43.

220. Transactions of the 1961 International Congress on Hypnosis. *The Nature of Hypnosis*, ed. M. V. KLINE. Foreword by LEWIS R. WOL-BERG. Institute for Research in Hypnosis and Postgraduate Center for Psychotherapy, New York, 1961.

221. Training in medical hypnosis. *J. Amer. med. Ass.*, 26 May 1962, **180**, 693–8.

222. VAN RENTERGHEM, A. W. *La psychothérapie dans ses différent modes*. Van Rossen, Amsterdam, 1907, 184 pp.

223. VIGDOROVITCH, M. V. Group suggestion as a method of preparing women for painless childbirth. (Kollektivnoie vnoushenie kak metod massovoi podgotovki beremennikh k obezbolievaniiou rodov). pp. 34–36 in *Proceedings of the Second Ukrainian Congress of Obstetrics and Gynaecology* (Tezissi Dokladov na II Oukrainskom Siezdie Akush i Ginec), Kiev, 1938 (in Russian).

224. VILLERS, CH. DE *Le Magnétiseur amoureux*, par un membre de la Société harmonique du régiment de Metz du Corps Royal de l'artillerie. Genève (Besançon), 1787, 229 pp.

225. VOGT, O. Zur Kenntnis des Wesens und der psychologischen Bedeutung des Hypnotismus. *Z. fuer Hypnotismus*, 1894–95, **3**, 277; 1896, **4**, 122–229.

226. VOLGYESI, F. *Menschen- und Tierhypnose*. Orell Fussli Verlag, Zurich and Leipzig, 2nd ed., 1963, 250 pp.

227. VOLGYESI, F. Ueber Aktiv-komplexe Psychotherapie und die Bewegung *"Schule der Kranken"*, VEB, Berlin, 1959, 186 pp.

228. VOUTSINAS, D. Hypnose, suggestion, hystérie. *Bull. Psychol.*, 1960, **13**, 122–229.

229. WATKINS, J. G. *Hypnotherapy of the War Neuroses*. Ronald Press, New York, 1949, 384 pp.

230. WEITZENHOFFER, A. M. *Hypnotism, an Objective Study in Suggestibility*. Wiley, New York, 1953, 380 pp.

231. WEITZENHOFFER, A. M. *General Techniques of Hypnotism*, Grune and Stratton, New York, 1957, 460 pp.

232. WEITZENHOFFER, A. M. The nature of hypnosis. Part I. *J. clin. Hypnosis*, 1963, **5**, 295–321.

233. WETTERSTRAND, O. G. *L'hypnotisme et ses applications à la médecine pratique* (French trans. by P. Valentin and T. Lindford), Octave Doin, Paris, 1899, 239 pp.

234. WHITE, R. W. A preface to the theory of hypnotism. *J. abnorm. soc. Psychol.*, 1941, **36**, 477–505.

235. WHITE, R. W. An analysis of motivation in hypnosis. *J. gen. Psychol.*, 1941, **24**, 145–62.

236. WOLBERG, L. *Medical Hypnosis*. vol. 1: *The Principles of Hypnotherapy;* vol. 2: *The Practice of Hypnotherapy*. Grune and Stratton, New York, 1948.

237. WOLBERG, L. *Hypnoanalysis*. Grune and Stratton, New York, 1945, 342 pp.

238. YOUNG, P. C. Hypnotic regression. Fact or artefact? *J. abnorm. soc. Psychol.*, 1940, **35**, 273–8.

239. ZDRAVOMYSLOV, V. I. *Experiments in the Application of Hypnosis in Obstetrics and Gynaecology*. (*Obezbolivanie Rodov Vnousheniem*). Medguiz, Leningrad, 1930, 30 pp. (in Russian).

Name Index

Ajuriaguerra 151
Ambrose 132, 135
Anna, O. 51, 52, 57, 140n., 147
Aubin-Gautier 22
Aubry 22, 23
August 135
Azam xiii, 28

Babinski xiii, 10, 10n., 21, 58
Bachet 11
Bailly 5n., 22, 23n.
Barber 25, 124n., 153n.
Baruk 11, 122
Baudoin 141
Beaunis 8, 16
Bechterev xiii
Bellak 41
Berillon 10n.
Bernard 8
Bernheim vii, xiii, 7, 8, 19, 25, 26, 27, 28, 48, 49, 56n., 58, 101, 104, 114
Bexton 34, 37
Birman 16, 17
Bleuler 120n.
Bonaparte, Marie 61n.
Bonfils 46
Boul 18
Bourguignon 38n.
Bourru 57, 58, 126, 140
Bowers 36n.
Braid xivn., 5, 12, 109
Bramwell 48
Brenman 28, 29n., 30, 33, 33n., 34, 35, 36, 37, 38, 41, 45, 48, 50, 53, 55, 59, 77, 95, 104, 115, 127, 134, 150, 151
Breuer 5, 51, 57, 58, 140, 147
Breuer, Mrs. 51, 52
Brodie 46
Brotteaux 11, 21, 122
Brouardel xiii, 21
Brown-Séquart 16
Burot 57, 58, 126, 140
Burq 8

Cahen, Michèle 151
Cahen, Muriel 31, 49
Chambard 11n., 122
Charcot xiii, xivn., 4n., 7, 8, 9, 10n., 21, 27, 52, 55, 154
Clark 135
Claude 89n.
Coué 10, 11, 20, 141
Crasilneck 153n.
Cuvellier 8n.
Czermak 42

Danilewski 42
Davis 101, 111, 129
Deckert 153n.
Déjerine 3, 56
De Jong 73, 89
D'Eslon 5, 5n.
Donato xivn., 4n.
Doniguevitch 132
Dorcus 19
Dubois 27, 56, 56n.
Dumontpallier xiii, 8, 9
Dupotet 6
Dupré 21n.

Enneis 134
Erickson 59, 104, 106, 126, 127, 134
Ey 47n., 142

Faria, Abbé 40
Faure 153
Felida 28
Fenichel 30, 147, 148
Ferenczi 9, 29, 38, 52
Figuier 144n.
Fisher 31
Flournoy 28
Forel xiii, 3, 88
Franklin 5n.
Freed 132, 135
Freud 3, 3n., 4n., 5, 8, 9, 28, 29, 38, 39, 44, 52, 57, 58, 64, 66, 67, 71, 88, 114, 140, 142, 146, 147, 148
Freud, Mrs. 55

Gachkel 11
Giliarovski 17
Gill 28, 29n., 30, 33, 33n., 34, 35, 36, 37, 38, 38n., 45, 48, 50, 53, 55, 59, 77, 95, 104, 115, 127, 134, 150, 151
Gorton 153n.
Grinberg 66, 67
Guillotin 5n.

Hadfield 58
Hall 153n.
Hallauer 122
Hansen xivn., 4n.
Hanson 46
Hartmann 34, 45
Hebb 33n., 34
Held 61n., 67
Heymons 43
Hilgard 62
Horsley 123
Horvai 17, 18
Hoskovec 18
Hull 19
Husband 101, 111, 129
Husson 10, 10n.

Israel 40
Ivanov-Smolenski 9, 17, 109

James 3
Janet xiii, xiv, 6, 7, 8, 10, 11, 28, 49, 54, 57, 58, 62, 125, 126, 140
Jones 30, 52, 58, 142, 147
Jussieu (de) 23

Kartamishev 65
Kauders 34, 40, 44, 54, 90, 134
Kaufman 49, 65
Kelly 81
Kennedy 70
King 36n.
Kircher 42, 43
Klein, Melanie 67
Klemperer 9
Kline 59
Klineberg 12
Knight 30, 77
Kohnstamm 99
Konstoroum 18, 57, 90

Koupernik xiv
Kramarz 40
Kretschmer 13, 40, 141
Kris 34
Kroger 132, 134, 135
Kubie 14, 33, 33n., 34, 34n., 35, 36. 37, 38, 41, 45, 47n., 49, 55, 127, 150. 151, 152, 154
Kurth 141, 152

Laclos 144n.
Ladame 69
Lafontaine 3n.
Lambling 46
Langen 141
Lassner 120n., 134
Lavoisier 5n.
Lebedinski 18, 88
Levy 46
Liberson 46
Liébeault vii, 6, 7, 8, 11, 16, 19, 21, 48, 49, 58, 101
Liégeois 8, 21
Lifchitz 58
Lilly 34
Lindner 59
Littré 12
Lombroso 3
Luthe 140
Luys 8, 109

Macalpine, Ida 31, 148, 149
McDougall 28
Magnan 3
Mahon 22
Mangold 42, 44
Margolin 32, 32n., 33, 33n., 34, 35, 36, 45, 55, 66, 150
Marguerite 22
Marie 126
Marmer 134
Meares 32, 109
Menninger 67
Mesmer 3, 4, 4n., 5, 5n., 6n., 20, 22, 22n., 23, 109, 132, 134, 139, 142, 143, 144, 145
Mesnet xiii
Montassut 11
Montserrat-Estève 11
Moreno 134
Moss 135

Moulinie 22
Mozart 3
Muhl 125
Murphy, Bridy 28n.

Nacht 32, 145
Newbold 132, 135
Newman 127
Nicolaiev 9

Orne 20, 21, 21n., 22, 24, 52
Oukhtomski 152

Padovani 11
Paracelsus 5, 5n.
Parcheminey xiv, 10
Pattie 19, 23
Pavlov 9, 16, 16n., 17, 18, 36n., 44, 45
Platonov 16, 17, 18
Popov 17
Porot 12
Preyer 42
Prince 28, 125
Puységur 4, 23, 132, 139, 144, 144n.

Rabaud 44
Reynolds, Mary 28
Rhodes 129, 131
Richet xiii, 11
Robertson 89
Rohmer 40
Rojnov 18
Rosen 60, 62

Salter 129
Sarbin 19, 20
Saussure (de) 142, 144n., 146
Schilder 13, 29, 30, 32, 34, 40, 43n., 44, 51, 54, 90, 134

Schneck 59
Schrenck-Notzing 3
Schultz 11, 13, 54, 134, 140, 141, 150, 151, 152
Shaw 135
Sidis 28
Simmel 58, 59
Slobodniak 18
Smith, Helen 28
Speer 106
Stewart 38, 39
Stokvis 40, 61, 74, 134, 141
Streltchouk 17
Sviadoshtsh 18
Svorad 18, 42, 44
Syrkine 132
Szasz 147

Terechkova, Valentina 34n.
Tokarsky 89
Tuckey 89

Van Renterghem 54, 132
Victor 23
Vigdorovitch 132
Villers (de) 23, 144, 144n., 145, 146
Vogt 51, 118
Voisin 88, 89
Volgyesi 18, 42
Voutsinas 4, 4n.

Wedenski 38n., 152
Weitzenhoffer 19, 24, 26, 129, 134
West 153n.
Wetterstrand 54, 132
White 19, 20
Wolberg 59, 105, 106, 115, 117, 118, 126, 129, 134

Zdravomyslov 132, 134

Subject Index

Académie Royale de Médecine 10
Academies of Medicine and Science
  (France) 5, 5n., 143
Academies of Medicine, Science and
  Education (U.S.S.R.) 17
Acting out 67
Addictions 74, 89–90
Agoraphobia 73
Alcoholism 89–90, 132
Alopecia 83
Alpha rhythm 41
American Medical Association 10,
  61, 69
American Psychiatric Association 9,
  70, 87
Amnesia 11, 22, 23, 86, 97, 114–16,
  120, 126
Anaesthesia 13, 21, 26, 84, 113, 114,
  129
Anaesthesiology 90, 134
Analgesia, hypnotic 39, 82, 90
Anamnesis 57, 95, 109
Angina pectoris 75
Animal magnetism 3–7, 12, 132, 139,
  143, 144, 144n., 146
Animism 5
Anorexia 6, 14
Anxiety 14, 31, 72, 84, 86, 90, 91,
  109
Aphonia 39, 86
Arm, heaviness of 111–12
Arm-rigidity 114–15, 131
Arrhythmia 74
Artefacts, ocular 41
Association, free 124, 125, 140
Asthma 49, 75
Attitude, practitioner's 95, 104, 105
Autogenic Training 11, 140–1,
  150–1
Autohypnosis 36n., 85, 128–31, 141,
  151
  fractionated 150
Automatism 28
Autosuggestion 11

Balance, impulse-defence 30, 38, 78
"Baquet", Mesmer's 22, 139
Barbiturates 123
Blindness, hysterical 77, 85
Blinking, post-hypnotic 116
Body-sway test 99–100
British Medical Association 9, 10, 12
Bronchitis 6
Burns 83, 90

Cancer 92
Catalepsy 8, 20, 20n., 123, 129
Cathartic method 4, 52, 56–57, 58,
  140, 140n.
Central nervous system 84
Childhood, memories of 125
Chloroform 122
Chlorpromazine 88
Chronaxia 38n.
Cold, feelings of 140
Colitis, ulcerative 76
Communication
  interpersonal 17
  "muscular" 152
  non-verbal 32, 96, 109
  unconscious 21
  verbal 4, 109, 144
Compulsions 26
Conflict, experimental 126–7
Confusional state, toxic 14
Congenital ichthyosiform
  erythrodermia of Brocq 84
Congenital linear naevus 84
Congenital pachyonychia 84
Constipation 14, 76
Counter-transference 4, 23, 29, 38,
  51, 52, 64, 65, 66, 73, 88, 95, 142,
  145, 151
"Crisis" 3, 4, 5, 20, 23, 57, 140
  simulated 23
Crystal gazing (mirror gazing) 125
Cure, criteria of 73–74
Cystitis 79

172

Deafness, hysterical 85
Defence(s) 31, 59, 63, 118, 123, 144, 147
Delusions 14, 87, 88, 89
Dementia, systematized 89
Dentistry 61, 84, 85, 134
Depression 14, 34, 75, 77, 88, 89, 91, 92
Deprivation, sensory 9n., 33n., 34, 34n., 35, 45, 47, 150
Dermatology 65, 83–84
Diarrhoea 6, 76, 91
Dissociation 28
Drawing, automatic 125
Dreaming, post-hypnotic 116
Dreams 59, 73, 124, 124n., 127
Drowsiness 103, 105
Drugs, effect at a distance 8
  hypnosis with 11, 55, 122–3
Dysphagia 86, 92

Eclampsia 83
Eczema 83
EEG 40
Ego 35, 41
  de-differentiation of 33
  self-excluding function of 41
Ego-apparatuses 34, 35
Ego-functioning 30
Ego-ideal 29, 39
Ego-psychology 9n., 30, 45
Enuresis 49, 78, 80, 81, 85
"Equalization phase" 16
Ether 122
Excitation, cortical 33
Expression, motor 95
Extraversion–introversion 49
Eyelid catalepsy 113

Fixation 30
Fluid, magnetic 3, 4, 146
Fluidism 3, 4, 5, 6–7, 139
"Folie à deux" 20–21, 21n.
Frequency, urinary 77, 80
Frigidity 79, 81
Frustration 31, 46

Gratification 29, 31, 38, 52, 54, 67, 119
Guilt 39

Gynecology 79

Hallucinations 21, 26, 34, 39, 57, 88, 97, 123
  negative 117
  positive sensory 116–17
Hand-clasp 99, 100, 131
Headache 84
Heaviness, feelings of 103, 119, 140, 141, 150
Herpes gestationis 84
  aesthesia 91, 113, 114
  suggestibility 21, 25
  ension, arterial 74
  igilance 41
  nalysis 56, 58–59, 64, 86, , 140
  rama 134
  dal phases" 16, 17

  3, 15, 25, 42–47
  n of 12–13
  nation (eye-gaze) 105–6
  levitation 106, 129
  l suggestion 105
  fixation 6, 103–5
  n the use of 61–63
  ed 118
  active 141
  2–3
  29, 51
  '9, 51
  ilschlaf) 13
Hy... ve Method 82, 132
Hyp... 82, 132
Hyp... 10, 12, 54, 60, 67, 72, 86, 87, 88, 89, 123, 134,

  ma... lication 139–40
Hypn...
  First ... nal Congress of, 1889 xiii, 57, 58, 69, 73
  Second International Congress of, 1902 73
Hypnotizability xiv, 43, 48–53, 88, 99, 101, 132, 139
  scale of (hypnotic suggestibility scoring system) 102
Hysteria xiv, 9, 11, 24, 50, 85

Identification 29, 39

Ideo-dynamism, law of (Bernheim) 19
Imagination 4, 5, 23, 42, 51, 59, 143
Imitation 23, 24
"Imitative theory" (Mesmer) 4
Immobility, hypnotic 45
Immobilization 43, 44, 45, 46
Impotence 79
Impulses, pre-genital 30
Incontinence 78, 81
Individual Psychology 74
Induction 32, 32n., 33, 37, 47, 55, 97n., 99, 101–10, 122
Infarction, cardiac 75
Inhibition 16n., 25, 33, 44
   cortical 40, 44
   partial 16
   restorative 54
Input, sensory 99
Insight 58, 65, 73, 74
Insomnia 31, 84, 92
Involvement, interpersonal 142, 145–7
Irritable bladder (cystalgie à urines claires) 77, 152
Isolation
   afferent 33
   partial afferent 34
   sensory 34

Kohnstamm's procedure 99

Lability, physiological 152
Laparotomy 25, 90
Lethargy 8
Love 144–5
Lumbago, traumatic 91

Mania, hysterical 88
Manic depressive disorder 88, 89
Manipulation, sensory-motor 33, 33n.
Masochism 33, 38
Mechanism
   schizo-paranoid 66
   self-protective 47n.
   trigger (trigger process) 38, 152
Medicine
   International Congress of Mental 58n.
   psychosomatic 14, 17, 74–85
Menopause 79

Menstruation 79
Metalloscopy 7–8
Metallotherapy 8, 146
Metals, "magnetic" 3
Metronome, use of 108–9
Muscular Tone, Active Control of 141
Myocarditis 75

Narcissism 30, 50
Narcoanalysis (narcosynthesis) 11, 76, 123
Narcosis, light barbiturate 123
Nausea 119
Nembutal 123
"Neurility" 6
Neurodermatitis 83
Neurosis (psychoneurosis) 14, 17, 51
   anxiety 86
   cardiac 75
   multiple conversion 86
   obsessional 73, 87, 118
   post-traumatic 90
   severe (borderline case) 87

Obesity 75
Obstetrics 82–83, 134
Oedipus complex 29, 33
Oliguria 74
Oncology 92

Parabiosis 38n.
"Paradoxical phase" 16
Paralysis 13, 85, 86
Parkinsonism 84
Passes 3, 6, 9, 139, 146
"Passive concentration" 146, 150
Pavlovian school 16
Pediatrics 85
Pentothal 123
Personality
   hypnotist's 51, 53
   hysterical 23, 86
   multiple 24
   restructuring of 55, 59, 142
   subject's 49
Persuasion 56, 56n., 132
"Phasic states" 16
Phobias 86, 87
Physiological Psychology, Congress of, 1889 58

Placebo 91, 123
Post-encephalitic states 13
Pre-sleep 40
Processes
  hypnotic 32
  symbolic 19
  transitional 38, 152
Psoriasis 83
Psychiatry, uses of hypnosis in
  85–90
Psychoanalysis 5, 15, 29–39, 45,
  64–68, 144–5, 149, 155
Psychodrama 134
Psychology
  Congress of (Third International
  Congress of Psychology), 1896
  61n.
  Congress of Experimental (Second
  International Congress of
  Psychology), 1892 58n.
  First International Congress of,
  1889 58, 58n.
Psychoneurosis (see Neurosis)
Psychoprophylactic method 82
Psychosis 17, 66, 87–89
  "hysterical" 88
Psychotherapy 7, 21–22, 24, 60, 64,
  65, 66, 67, 70, 71, 74, 75, 78, 79,
  85, 106, 139, 142, 149, 150
  evaluation of 73–74
  group 3, 132, 134
  "on demand" 78
Psychotherapies, psychoanalytically
  oriented 64–65, 73
Pyelitis of pregnancy 82

Rapport 3, 4, 9, 16, 142
Reality principle 39
Reality testing 39
Re-education 56, 59
Reflex
  nauseous 84
  patellar 40
  tonic 44
Regression 30, 31, 34, 35, 38, 41, 46,
  47, 54, 57n., 59, 62, 66, 73, 84, 91,
  123, 125, 140, 149, 150, 151
Relationship
  archaic 35, 151
  dentist–patient 61
  doctor–patient 10, 69, 139, 141–52
  hypnotic 9, 20, 29, 31, 55, 63, 65,
  72

interpersonal 33n., 36, 143, 146
  psychoanalytic 31, 66
  psychotherapeutic 3, 12, 29n., 31,
  60, 110, 145
  verbal 144
Relaxation 46, 97, 99, 101, 103, 113,
  115, 132, 150, 151
Re-orientation 59
Report
  Bailly 23
  secret 23, 143
Resistances 59, 142
Restraint technique 46
Retention, urinary 78, 79, 90
Reticular formation 40
Reverie 34, 124
Rhythm, cardiac and respiratory 140
Rigidity (of muscles) 13
Ritual, obsessive 87
Role-taking (role-playing) 19, 20–21,
  23

Salpêtrière school 8, 19
"Schizomania" 89n.
Schizophrenia 36n., 87–88
Sclerosis, multiple 84
Scopochloralose 11, 21, 122–3
Signalling system, second 17
Simulation xiii, 14, 23
Sleep xiv, 8n., 12, 15, 26, 27, 40–41,
  54, 103, 120, 141
  incomplete or partial 12, 13, 16, 27
Smoking, excessive 89
"Somatization" 150
Somnambulism 4, 8, 14, 22, 23–24,
  28, 49, 97, 118, 124, 144
"Sophrose" 12
Spasms, oesophagal and cardiac 76
Stammering 84
Stimulation, symbolic 19
Stimuli
  auditory 9, 108, 119
  luminous 109
  monotonous 95, 150
  negative 16
  suggestive 149
  tactile 9
  thermal 9, 109
  verbal 13, 119
  visual 9
Stress 46, 68
Submissiveness 109

Suggestibility   19, 25, 26, 27, 49, 65,
    99, 122, 148, 149
  tests of   99–100
Suggestion   xiv, 4, 7, 9, 10, 11, 13, 21,
    25, 28, 54, 55, 56n., 57, 62, 65, 66,
    73, 75, 76, 84, 85, 89, 90, 91, 97n.,
    99, 103, 104, 110, 122, 139, 140,
    141, 142, 148, 149, 150, 151
  non-verbal   11
  post-hypnotic   31, 76, 82, 114, 116,
    119, 125, 129
  post-narcotic   123
  "reasoned"   56
  verbal   6, 11, 20, 26, 31, 49, 108,
    123
Suggestive phase   16
Superego   39
Sympathy   142
Symptoms
  conversion   122
  substitute   63, 73, 92
  transfer by magnets   8
  treatment of   57
System
  cardio-vascular   74, 82
  circulatory   25
  endocrine   75
  gastro-intestinal   25, 76
  genito-urinary   77–82
  respiratory   75
  sensory   25

Therapy
  by hypnosis   54
  drug   142
  play   125
  under hypnosis   54
Thyroidectomy   90
Tics   84
Training, autodidactic   129
Trance   11, 13–14, 20, 21, 30–31, 39,
    59, 77, 101, 111–18, 119, 120–1,
    124, 125, 128, 129, 132

Transference   9, 29, 30, 31, 32, 32n.,
    33, 33n., 34, 36, 37, 38, 50, 59,
    61n., 65, 73, 87, 88, 98, 142, 143.
    145, 146, 147, 148, 149, 150, 151
  autogenous, endogenous or
    anonymous   36, 37
  heterogenous, exogenous or
    personalized   36, 37
  "wild"   142
Traumatology   90–92
Treatment
  anaclitic   66
  prolonged sleep   74
Trees, magnetized   141

Ulcer, duodenal or gastric   76
"Ultraparadoxical phase"   16
"Umschaltung" (change of attitude)
    54, 150, 152
Urology   77
Urticaria   83

Vaginismus   79
"Voluntarists"   144
Vomiting   6, 76
  of pregnancy   82

Waking points   16
Waking zone   16
Warmth, feelings of   103, 131, 140,
    141, 150
Warts   83
Water, magnetized   7
Whooping-cough   6
Working through   54, 73
Writer's cramp   73
Writing, automatic   59, 125

Zoomagnetism   6–7